The Clinician's Guide to

SUBSTANCE USE DISORDERS

Practical Tools for Assessment, Treatment & Recovery

Paul Brasler, LCSW, CAIP

Copyright © 2022 Paul Brasler

Published by
PESI Publishing, Inc.
3839 White Ave
Eau Claire, WI 54703

Cover Design: Emily Dyer
Editing: Jenessa Jackson, PhD
Layout: Emily Dyer and Alissa Schneider

ISBN: 9781683735670 (print)
ISBN: 9781683735687 (epub)
ISBN: 9781683735694 (epdf)

PESI Publishing
pesipublishing.com

For Mom,
Reverend Keitha Lynne Brasler
1948–2019

Table of Contents

Acknowledgments

I thank God for my life and the people who are in my life.

Claire, my beautiful wife of 20 years and counting. We still make each other laugh.

Sam, Ben, and Eli, my three mighty sons. I am honored to be your dad. Thanks for sacrificing some of our time together so I could write.

Andy McAllister (and the Blackhearts), Mark Miller, Randy Frederick (and everyone at Alchemy Wellness), Redeemer Anglican Church, Adam Creveling, Ashley Harrell, Priscilla Witwer, Marc Leslie, and Kevin and Manda Gibson.

The wonderful folks at PESI, specifically Claire Zelasko for giving me a shot at working for PESI and to Jenessa Jackson for her editing skills. A HUGE thank you to Kate Sample for shepherding this project from the beginning. Y'all are awesome!

This book is dedicated to my mother, the Reverend Keitha Brasler. Mom raised three boys on her own while attending college and seminary, all while working full-time. The last 19 years of her career were as a hospital chaplain, where she sat with people as they died, comforting them and their families. Mom died in December 2019 after giving cancer one hell of a fight. She ministered to staff in her hospital from her deathbed, never missing a step. She had a heart for people living with challenges, including substance use disorders. I hope this book is something she would have turned to for information and hope. I miss you, Mom.

Introduction

When I was a student in a Master of Social Work (MSW) program, I had to apply for my first internship, and I was asked which population I would *not* want to work with. Being a trusting and naïve person, I wrote (in all capital letters): "ADDICTS, BECAUSE THEY CAN HELP IT!"

Let me explain my response. Prior to entering graduate school, and throughout my journey through the MSW program, I worked exclusively with children and adolescents. In particular, I worked in a homeless shelter for teens and in a residential treatment program for "emotionally disturbed" adolescents. Many of these kids had been removed (or had run away) from their families or foster homes because of parental or caregiver substance use. I assumed that adults who used drugs were bad, and I wanted nothing to do with them.

In reaction to my response to the placement query, the school placed me in a residential treatment program for women who were heroin dependent. The internship took place during a hot Richmond summer, and when I first stepped foot into my new place of business, I wondered how it had avoided being condemned. It had no air conditioning, the plumbing was unreliable, and it reeked of sweat, urine, sewage, and fried bologna (served at least once daily). As I sweat through my shirt my first morning in the internship, I wondered what I'd done to deserve the placement. In retrospect, that summer, and all I learned while working with the women there, would shape my entire career as a social worker.

As I got to know some of the women in the facility, especially those who became my clients, I realized that their stories were the *same* as the stories of the kids I'd worked with. The only difference was that my clients were adults, not kids. All of them had hauntingly comparable stories of horrific abuse, neglect, rage, isolation, and regret. But the cry from each person was the same: *I did not choose this—I want something different!*

Following my internship, I began to research commonly used drugs, and I started to understand how substances had negatively affected certain people in my life, leading to early deaths for some. I even considered my own use of alcohol at a younger age and how I had come perilously close to sliding into self-destruction myself. But even in the difficult research of substance use, I learned about opportunities for recovery. Years later, I began to learn how some plants and chemicals can be helpful to people looking for wholeness and repossession of their lives. My research forced me to discover there was much more to substance use than I had once thought.

Throughout this journey of learning, I have developed **five keys to remember when working with people with substance use disorders (SUD):**

1. You must like people. If you don't like people, this book is not for you. No training, class, or book can teach you how to care about people—this comes from you, your story, and your values.

2. People are worthy of help, have the right to self-determination, and should be treated with respect.

3. Your role is to walk with your clients—not live their lives for them—and to respect their choices, even when you disagree with those choices.

4. No one sets out to become addicted to substances or behaviors.

5. Recovery is possible and is defined by the client.

Perhaps your journey is like mine: You find yourself working with people with SUD and were never trained how to work with this population. Or maybe you work in the SUD field and want to learn more. It could be that you are simply curious (and that is okay).

Regardless of your reasons for picking up this book, my hope is to provide you with the knowledge and tools necessary to be better equipped for the current addiction crisis. Although addiction crises have occurred throughout human history, the current crisis began in the mid-1990s with the over prescription of opioids, and it continues today with record deaths from heroin, cocaine, methamphetamine, fentanyl, and other "novel" substances (Macy, 2018; Quinones, 2015).

One of the contributing factors to this crisis is the lack of addiction education in medical schools, nursing schools, and behavioral health programs. For example, less than 15 percent of social work schools offer specialized programs in substance use, and an overwhelming number don't even include courses on the topic at all (Wilkey et al., 2013). Not surprisingly, the addiction crisis has caused a growing need for trained professionals with substance use backgrounds. But educational systems have simply not provided a match for the demand, leading to what can only be described as an "institutional denial or minimization" (Quinn, 2010, p. 8). This book is an effort to provide much-needed information for clinicians who may not have received substantial training in the addiction and substance use fields.

WHAT'S IN THIS BOOK?

The Clinician's Guide to Substance Use Disorders is for anyone working in a professional capacity who wants to learn more about SUD, its treatments, and its recovery process. While I designed this book for mental health providers, it is equally helpful to people working in medical settings, educational institutions, the legal system, religious settings, and other fields. In writing this book, I tried to keep in mind what I would like to have known when I started working in the field (but could not find an in accessible source):

- Which substances do people become addicted to? How do these plants and chemicals work? How are they similar and different from one another?

- Why do some people develop SUD while others do not?

- How does SUD impact the entire person?

- How can I work with someone with SUD if I have never used the substances they have used (or are using)?

- What are the connections between mental illness and SUD?

- What can I do to help loved ones who have been impacted by someone else's SUD?

After working with people with SUD for over 20 years, I continue to ask questions and have found that my clients are the best teachers. In fact, the more I learn about SUD, the more I realize I have a lot left to learn. The SUD treatment field is very much the same way, so this book details what experts know now, respectfully understanding that knowledge on the subject will continue to develop.

This book is organized into 12 chapters, as follows:

- **Chapter 1: Setting a Foundation**

  How we think and talk about our clients shapes how we treat them. This chapter examines the language of SUD treatment, including definitions of addiction and recovery. A brief overview of some of the theories underlying SUD is provided. The chapter concludes with case study exercises to help clinicians understand the progression of SUD.

- **Chapter 2: The Science Behind Substance Use Disorders**

  This chapter begins with a discussion of the biopsychosocial-spiritual approach to understanding and treating SUD. It then discusses the close relationship between a client's SUD and their trauma history. The last part covers the basic neurobiology of substance use.

- **Chapter 3: Substances of Use**

  This chapter examines common substances that people use, including various plants and chemicals that can change how people think, act, and feel. It also includes information regarding different intoxication and withdrawal syndromes, which is essential for clinicians to provide safe, appropriate, and compassionate care.

- **Chapter 4: Assessment of Substance Use Disorders**

  Quality, individualized treatment cannot take place without a comprehensive assessment. This chapter delves into various screening tools that can assist in identifying which clients need a SUD assessment; it then helps provide a complete SUD, mental health, trauma, and medical assessment for your client. The chapter ends with an examination of drug screens and their place in treatment.

- **Chapter 5: Co-Occurring Disorders**

  Many clients with SUD have co-occurring behavioral health disorders. Therefore, clinicians should always be asking themselves this question: Is what I am seeing in my client the result of a substance or a mental health problem (or both)? This chapter explores some of the mental health disorders commonly seen with SUD.

- **Chapter 6: Treatment Planning—Determining the Correct Level of Care**

  After the assessment phase, clinicians need to determine which level of treatment best meets their client's needs within the least-restrictive environment. This chapter examines the various levels of SUD treatment as outlined by the American Society of Addiction Medicine and discusses which level of care is appropriate for each client. The chapter ends with the role of pharmacotherapy in treatment with a focus on medications for opioid use disorder.

- **Chapter 7: Strategies to Improve Client Engagement**

  Motivational interviewing (MI) created a significant mindset change when it emerged in the field of SUD treatment decades ago. This chapter examines several MI strategies that will help clinicians engage their clients. It also addresses the process of relapse and examines ways that relapse can be limited. The chapter closes with a discussion of strategies that can help retain clients in treatment.

- **Chapter 8: Individual Cognitive Behavioral Therapy**

  According to the cognitive model of substance use, SUD is a learned behavior that can be addressed through cognitive behavioral therapy (CBT), which targets the underlying beliefs that contribute to substance use behavior. While CBT is not the only form of therapy for SUD, it can be effective in changing the thought processes that promote continued substance use versus recovery. This chapter will examine some of the basic principles of CBT and the steps involved in the cognitive model of substance use.

- **Chapter 9: Substance Use Disorders and the Family**

  When a family member has SUD, it affects the entire family in numerous ways. This chapter examines the roles and rules commonly found in family systems impacted by SUD. It also tackles the question: When does helping someone with SUD turn into enabling? The second part of the chapter describes approaches to engaging and treating families with SUD.

- **Chapter 10: Group Therapy Strategies**

  Although group therapy is commonly used in SUD treatment, many clinicians have limited training or experience with this modality. This chapter will help you understand group dynamics, the roles of group members, and how to run different types of groups. The chapter also discusses Alcoholics Anonymous and other 12-step (and peer-related) support groups.

- **Chapter 11: Treatment Strategies for Special Populations**

  In the beginnings of SUD treatment, services were designed to meet the needs of middle- to upper-class, heterosexual, White men. We now know that SUD impacts everyone differently, and each group of people have specific needs when it comes to SUD treatment. These groups include (but are not limited to) women, adolescents, ethnic and cultural minorities, the LGBTQ+ community, older adults, and others.

- **Chapter 12: Legal and Ethical Issues in SUD Treatment**

  Which laws, policies, and ethical principles impact SUD treatment? Should an agency's practice adhere to the Title 42 of the Code of Federal Regulations Part 2 guidelines or to the Health Insurance Portability and Accountability Act? This chapter helps you understand the legal aspects of SUD treatment. It also examines answers to the question: How do I respond when a client asks me if I'm in recovery? This chapter closes by looking at the impact of stigma on SUD treatment and examining ways that clinicians can care for themselves as they walk with their clients.

In addition to the information presented in each chapter, you'll find a variety of tools included throughout this book. These tools are not meant to be used in any precise order. Quality SUD treatment is individualized, so you should select the specific tools you need for each client. The five different tools included in this book are as follows:

- **Clinician handouts** are intended for clinician reference and are meant as a supplement for the content covered in each chapter. Many client worksheets and handouts reference material found in the clinician handouts, so I recommend that you familiarize yourself with these handouts before using the worksheets.

- **Clinician exercises** provide learning activities for clinicians to review their knowledge from the chapter and put this knowledge to practical use.

- **Clinician forms** provide a template for clinicians to use when conducting a mental health or substance use assessment or screening.

- **Client handouts** provide supplementary material for clients to read to emphasize the material being covered.

- **Client worksheets** are educational activities for clients to use during or outside a session. Clients can complete this worksheet with a clinician, a peer recovery specialist, another provider, or on their own. There are no wrong answers. Make sure to familiarize yourself with the chapter content that the worksheets are based upon before introducing them to clients.

When people find out that I work with people with SUD, they often say something like, "Wow, that must be tough work!"

"It is," I reply. "But it is the coolest thing I've ever done professionally."

Sometimes the conversation ends there, as many people who feel insulated from SUD do not want to dwell on it. For many people, addiction is something that happens to other people, but it would never happen to them.

However, when someone is curious about my work and asks me to elaborate, I point out that SUD is about *we*, not *them* versus *us*. SUD does not affect only people with SUD and their immediate circles; it touches all aspects of our society. Moreover, individuals with SUD are not bad people—they are some of the smartest, most adaptive, and most incredibly resilient people I've ever met. I am honored that they allow me to walk alongside them in their journey. I hope each of my clients can learn something from me. I know for sure that I learn a lot from them.

I want you to walk with people with SUD. My hope is that this book will be the resource you need to empower your clients on their journey toward recovery.

1

Setting a Foundation

THE POWER OF LANGUAGE

How we talk *about* a person, and how we talk *with* a person, determines how we *treat* that person. When it comes to SUD, language can make a world of difference. So often, people with SUD are labeled as no more than a "drunk," a "junkie," or a "crackhead." When people with substance use disorder are dehumanized in this way, they come to internalize these labels and view themselves as no more than their addiction. Facing this societal rejection and discrimination, even from health care professionals, can make them less likely to seek help. And if they do seek help, they are likely to receive less-than-compassionate treatment (e.g., incarceration vs. rehabilitation).

It is important to use person-centered language, rather than deficit-based language, to reflect the sentiment that people are more than their problems. Person-centered language places the emphasis on the individual, as opposed to their disorder—for example, referring to a client as "someone who has SUD" versus an "addict." But by focusing only on someone's disorder, using deficit-based language, we can begin to see them as less than a person and more of a problem. We are often quick to blame someone with SUD and tend to view their problems as being all their fault. While personal choice forms a part of a person's SUD (e.g., the choice to enter treatment), there are many factors that create and sustain SUD as a whole.

Ultimately, deficit-based language makes clinicians more likely to recommend punitive treatment approaches (Herron & Brennan, 2020) and perpetuates stigma toward people with SUD, which is a major barrier for people seeking treatment. Language drives stigma, so if we change how we talk with (and about) others, we can decrease the stigma around SUD and SUD treatment. This is not about being politically correct; it is about attracting people to treatment.

Preferred Terminology:
Person-Centered Language for SUD

Instead of saying...	Consider...
Abuse	Use
Addict	Person who uses drugs
User	or
Crackhead	Person with a substance use disorder
Dope fiend	
Junkie	
Addiction	Substance use disorder
Clean	In recovery
	or
	Testing negative
Dirty	Testing positive
Medication-assisted treatment	Pharmacotherapy
Medication maintenance	or
Substitution treatment	Medication for opioid use disorder
Relapse	Return to use

Although *addiction* is generally not considered person-centered language, the term is sometimes used in the current literature, so when I quote a source, it may include the older terminology. In addition, clients may talk about their "clean time" as a measure of how long they have been in recovery—or use other terms to describe themselves that I would not ordinarily use—and I do not correct them for this. Indeed, language can be an opportunity to connect with clients. Here's an example from a conversation I had with a client, who we'll call Sam:

Sam:	My name is Sam, and I'm a junkie.
Me:	It's nice to meet you, Sam. Thanks for coming in. How else do you describe yourself?
Sam:	What do you mean?
Me:	Well, you've told me a little about the problem that brings you here, but what else can you tell me about yourself? Your family? What do you do for a living? What are some things you like to do?
Sam:	I've never thought about that. Usually when I come to these treatment places, all they want to talk about is my addiction.
Me:	Well, yes, treating SUD is one of the things our clinic does, but we want people coming here to know that we see them as more than the things they're struggling with. That being said, how else do you describe yourself?
Sam:	Well…I'm an artist.
Me:	What kind of medium?
Sam:	I draw, paint, and I used to be a photographer…

In this example, the client initially described himself as a "junkie," and I used this as an opportunity to uncover more about how Sam viewed his identity. I wanted to show Sam that I saw him as more than his SUD and that I wanted to connect with him as a person, not "just an addict." People are more than their problems, but we may still struggle with this concept when it comes to people with SUD. Reasons for this include outdated information or myths and stereotypes about SUD, which contribute to the continued stigma associated with it.

MYTHS AND STEREOTYPES OF SUBSTANCE USE DISORDER

The following table provides some harmful myths and stereotypes about SUD. Along with each falsity is a statement that more accurately represents the situation. Myths like these often serve as a barrier for people with SUD to get well, so it is important to dispel misinformation and get the facts straight.

Myth or Stereotype	Reality
Drug use alone causes SUD.	People can use substances without developing SUD (e.g., a person having a glass of wine with dinner). One of the challenges of this field is to understand the ways that disparate factors (including exposure to drugs) work together to cause certain people to develop SUD.
Drug treatment does not work.	If we were to view treatment as a one-time intervention, then this myth would be true. But SUD is a chronic condition, so treatment often needs to be more than a single intervention, and in many cases, some form of support is needed indefinitely. Just as SUD takes time to develop, so does treatment and recovery.
We are winning the "war on drugs."	No, we are not. One of the main reasons this is false is that drugs are seen as a problem that can be solved by stopping the supply. This means waging war on the people who use drugs, which only widens poverty, diverts resources away from treatment and education, and costs lives. With criminal justice reform and increased resources for prevention and treatment, perhaps we can move closer to a day when drug use is less destructive to our communities and viewed as something to be treated instead of punished.
Addiction is completely a choice. Addiction is dependent on a person's genetic makeup.	Neither of these statements is completely true or false. People are not automatons who follow their genetic programming irrespective of their environment and life experiences. Likewise, SUD does not arise solely due to the choices that a person makes. People are impacted by their genetic predispositions *and* can make choices, specifically ones such as pursuing treatment and recovery.
Most people with SUD are homeless or unemployed.	Most people with SUD are *housed and employed*. However, people with SUD often minimize their illness by comparing themselves to people who have lost everything due to drug use. They may rationalize something like: "It can't be *that* bad or I'd be out on the streets." Many times, it *is* that bad, but the person has resources that lessen the impact of their SUD.

Myth or Stereotype	Reality
A person will only stop using drugs when they "hit rock bottom."	We once thought that the only time a person would stop using drugs was when they lost everything and were faced with the choices of prison, death, or recovery. We now know that "rock bottom" means different things to each person and that someone doesn't need to lose everything to say, "I am ready to try to make some changes."
A person can love someone enough to change them.	Few things are as hard as watching a person you love struggle with a SUD. When we love someone, we do whatever it takes to help them. However, love alone will not change another person's behaviors. This does not mean that we should detach and not help them; it means we must help them in a different manner than we think is helpful.

ADDICTION DEFINED

Addiction is a treatable, chronic medical disease involving complex interactions among brain circuits, genetics, the environment, and an individual's life experiences. People with addiction use substances or engage in behaviors that become compulsive and often continue despite harmful consequences. Prevention efforts and treatment approaches for addiction are generally as successful as those for other chronic diseases.

—Adopted by the American Society of Addiction Medicine (ASAM) Board of Directors
September 15, 2019

The ASAM's definition reflects the movement to view addiction in a medicalized way, which is necessary to encourage health care providers to view SUD as a chronic illness (like hypertension and diabetes) rather than a moral failing. However, I think that in emphasizing the medical aspects of SUD, we can lose sight of the complexity of the problem. For this reason, I like the following definition:

Addiction is a multi-determined phenomenon with layers within layers of mutual influences, internal and external, all interacting concurrently, leading to a pathological outcome. It is no more true [sic] to say that addiction is simply a brain disease, or a flawed personal choice, or an experience of learning than it is to say that falling in love is nothing but biochemistry. (Morgan, 2019, p. 4)

What Is Addiction?

Addiction (also known as substance use disorder) means different things to different people. Use the following questions to consider what addiction means to you and how you think other people view it.

Which words, names, or thoughts come to mind when you hear the word *addiction*? (Quickly write down as many things as you can.)

Draw a picture of addiction.

How would you define addiction?

What are things that people can become addicted to?

Do you think that society has a negative view of people with addiction? Why or why not?

What are some questions about addiction that you would like answered?

SUBSTANCE USE DISORDER DEFINED

The term *addiction* more formally refers to a diagnosis of SUD, which is a disorder that first appeared in the fifth edition of the *Diagnostic and Statistical Manual of Mental Disorders* (DSM-5; American Psychiatric Association [APA], 2013). This new diagnosis compressed the previous categories of substance abuse and substance dependence that appeared in earlier versions of the DSM. This caused some controversy in the SUD treatment community because the new diagnostic category no longer separated the behavioral aspects of substance use (i.e., abuse) from the physiological symptoms of substance use (i.e., dependence). This meant that someone who had just started using a substance would be diagnosed with the same disorder as someone (with many more symptoms) who had been using for decades.

To be diagnosed with SUD, a person must exhibit at least two of the following symptoms within a 12-month period. These symptoms include using the substance for a longer period of time than intended, unsuccessfully attempting to quit or curb use, spending excessive time using (or recovering from use), failing to meet life obligations due to use, and continuing to use despite the problems that it causes. In addition, people with SUD often stop participating in activities that they used to enjoy because of their use and may also use in dangerous situations (e.g., driving while under the influence). Finally, because of the physiological dependence that can develop with continued use, it is common for individuals with SUD to develop cravings, tolerance, and withdrawal symptoms. Be aware that some of the symptoms may differ depending on the substance in question (APA, 2013).

Polysubstance Use

It is not unusual for people with SUD to use more than one drug at a time, which is known as *polysubstance use*. For example, people who use stimulants, like cocaine or methamphetamine, may use alcohol or opioids to calm themselves after prolonged stimulant use. Others may use stimulants and opioids together because doing so extends the length of the stimulant high and decreases the severity of the "nod" (falling asleep) associated with opioid use. In addition, people who are dependent on one substance in a drug class can become dependent on other drugs in that class, a process sometimes called *cross dependence*.

A few years ago, when I was managing a medication assistance program for people with opioid use disorder, we noticed that some of our clients were taking their Suboxone® (a medication used to treat opioid addiction) as prescribed, but they were also using cocaine. Some of these clients were adamant that they had not used cocaine regularly prior to starting Suboxone, and a few wondered if Suboxone caused them to use. Thankfully, this was brought up in a treatment group, which allowed us the chance to provide some education that Suboxone does not cause a craving for cocaine. Our peer recovery specialist then helped the group realize that most people with SUD are chasing a high, regardless of the high being due to an opioid, stimulant, or other substance. We should, therefore, not be surprised when clients use more than one substance, as this is far more common than most people outside of the SUD population realize.

Levels of Drug Use

"How do I know if I am using too much?" "When does my use become a *problem*?" I have been asked questions like these countless times—usually not by clients but by friends or acquaintances. Although it is easy for our society to want to quantify what constitutes a problem (e.g., "Five is not a problem, but six is."), doing so would be inaccurate. Therefore, my typical response to such questions is, "It depends." And my response is based in truth; each person is different, and it's not how much a person uses (or how often they use or what they use) but rather *how their use impacts them*. This is where we begin to look at the levels of substance use. Keep in mind that these levels are not set in stone and that people can move fluidly throughout the levels.

Levels of Drug Use

Level (Morgan, 2019)	Intervention
Contemplation: Person consciously and/or unconsciously questions and prepares for use, including observation.	Provide information about substances, including associated risks.
Experimentation: Person tries a substance for the first time.	Provide information about substances, including associated risks.
First experience of intoxication: Person may or may not like this experience, then may explore other options or stop use altogether.	Provide psychoeducation on why people use substances and exploration of how to recognize if continued use becomes a problem.
A **relationship** forms with the substance, which for many people is stable and does not create negative consequences (e.g., moderate drinking).	Provide psychoeducation on why people use substances and exploration of how to recognize if continued use becomes a problem.
Misuse (abuse): Person uses secretively or impulsively and continues to use despite negative consequences. However, there is no evidence of tolerance or withdrawal symptoms.	Provide counseling interventions (e.g., motivational interviewing [MI], CBT).
Dependence: The body adapts to the substance, such that the person experiences withdrawal symptoms in the absence of the substance and develops a tolerance to the substance.*	Provide counseling interventions (e.g., MI, CBT, individual, family, group), pharmacotherapy (e.g., methadone), withdrawal management protocols for some substances.
Substance use disorder (addiction): The person experiences the chemical aspects of dependence and tolerance, as well as the behavioral components of cravings, compulsions, impaired control, ignoring of consequences, and a chronic course.	Same as dependence, but some individuals may also require intensive outpatient treatment, partial hospitalization, or residential treatment.

* Dependence is a physiological process that also occurs with medications that are not addictive. Examples include antidepressants, insulin, and other medications. Persons taking these medications experience tolerance and withdrawal symptoms but do not experience a compulsion to use.

ORIGINS OF SUBSTANCE USE DISORDER

When we look at the factors that cause SUD, a simple, concise explanation rarely defines something so complex. Part of this difficulty is society's stigmatization of SUD, as most of us were taught at an early age that drugs were bad and that was it. We came to infer that if drugs were bad, then the people who used them must be bad as well. Our view was further supported by laws that consider substance use a moral failing that is worthy of incarceration. However, if we look at SUD from a historical and anthropological view, we learn that SUD is as complex as the individuals and societies it impacts.

To begin, throughout history, people have used plants and chemicals to change how they think, feel, and act. This is described in early writings, including the Bible, Egyptian hieroglyphics, and other sources. Various plants and mushrooms used to create intoxicating effects can be found in artwork from ancient civilizations around the world. Substance use is not a new phenomenon.

Beginning as early as the seventeenth century, physicians came to realize that some people may have a predisposition toward SUD (White, 2014). We now know that substance use can arise as a result of possible genetic patterns, learned behaviors, a response to stressors, or some combination of these. What is clear is that SUD is not a simple problem that can be blamed on a person's poor choices. The cause of SUD instead lies somewhere along the spectrum in the long-standing debate of nature versus nurture. In other words, are we born thinking, acting, and feeling the way we do, or do we only develop these patterns based on our experiences? Or perhaps it is somewhere in between?

Most people would agree there are elements of nature *and* nurture that shape us. For example, I worked with an 18-year-old young man who was part of a family where SUD was firmly entrenched. He lived in an environment where there was a high concentration of drugs, and the use of substances was accepted (and even encouraged). To understand how this permeated his lineage, we sat down one day and completed an extensive genogram—a graphical representation of familial history of behavior patterns—with help from his mother. Together, we went back six generations and saw how every male in his family had alcohol use disorder, and half the females had a SUD. It stunned this young man (and me), and we wondered if his struggles with substances were due to his genetic makeup, his environment, or both.

In addition, we cannot talk about SUD without acknowledging that the use of some drugs has become relatively socially acceptable (e.g., alcohol, cannabis, caffeine) and that our understanding of which drugs are considered appropriate changes over time. For instance, when I was growing up in the 1970s and '80s, cigarette smoking was common; there were even smoking areas in my high school for students. This is no longer the case for cigarettes, but look at today's society—cannabis is more widely accepted and alcohol remains as popular as ever.

Finally, we must consider that many people start using drugs because it feels good at first. Although these feel-good experiences drive the initial attraction to substances, soon the avoidance of withdrawal symptoms becomes the motivating factor for continued use. When we consider all of these factors, the origins of SUD are less clear-cut than many have been led to believe.

Test Your Knowledge of SUD

1. What is the most used mind-altering chemical in the world?

2. Which mind-altering chemical kills the most people each year in the United States?

3. Which substance brings the most people to the emergency department each year in the United States?

4. Name at least five ways a person can put a substance into their body.

5. Of these ways, which method gets the chemical to a person's brain the quickest?

6. What is the biggest risk factor for a person who suddenly stops consuming alcohol or other central nervous system depressants after prolonged use?

7. What is a speedball?

8. What is the name of a medicine that can reverse an opioid overdose?

True or False

9.   T or F   Cocaine and crack are two different substances.

10. T or F   The current opioid crisis began in 2014.

11. T or F   Snorting heroin is safer than injecting it.

12. T or F   Most standard urine drug screens can detect all substances of use.

13. T or F   A person experiencing alcohol withdrawal is at a higher risk of death than a person experiencing opioid withdrawal.

14. T or F   Most babies born to mothers who use heroin and other opioids will experience neonatal opioid withdrawal syndrome (NOWS).

15. T or F   People who use medications like methadone or Suboxone to stop using heroin or other opioids are not really in recovery.

16. T or F   Regular use of cannabis is harmless.

You can find an answer key to these questions at the end of this chapter.

SELECTED THEORIES OF SUBSTANCE USE DISORDER

In the following section, I focus on the prevalent theories of SUD. While I admit that I am probably leaving some good theories out, the ones included here will help guide our discussion of specific treatment interventions in the coming chapters.

Moral Model

Beginning in the late 1700s, alcohol use disorder (commonly referred to as *alcoholism*) was recognized as a chronic medical condition that could be held at bay by not drinking. Treatment for alcohol use disorder, opioid use disorder, and other forms of substance use looked promising as government organizations and private entities focused on rehabilitation and recovery, not punishment, to address SUD (White, 2017). However, this situation took a turn in the early twentieth century when new views of addiction placed the causes on underlying psychiatric conditions, poor moral character, or bad choices made by the person. Quite often, these views were grounded in racism, classism, and fear of certain immigrant groups (Hari, 2015). These views represented the basis of the moral model, which maintains that substance use is a moral failing or character defect (Avery & Avery, 2019):

In turn, treatment was replaced by prohibition and the criminalization of addiction. However, as we have seen over the past 50 years, we cannot arrest and incarcerate our way out of society's SUD problem. Despite increasing arrest rates for drug possession in the past, drug use has continued to grow (Hari, 2015). Furthermore, the complete prohibition of these drugs is not warranted, as most can be effective when used medically or appropriately. For instance, opioids are used to treat pain, stimulants can treat attention-deficit/hyperactivity disorder (ADHD), and other drugs, like hallucinogens and cannabinoids, have been used to help with depression, anxiety, and other problems since before written history (Pollan, 2018).

Biopsychosocial Model

By the middle of the twentieth century, following the repeal of the national prohibition of alcohol, addiction treatment regained traction in the United States. An important realization that emerged from this movement was that many people who struggled with substances continued to do so even after losing everything in their lives. This led to new views of SUD as something more than a person's poor choices or misguided character. What emerged was the biopsychosocial model, which maintains that there are multiple biological, psychological, and social factors that can contribute to addiction (Avery & Avery, 2019):

Subsequent models and theories of SUD are derived from this model.

Medical or Disease Model

The nationwide prioritization of addiction treatment and recovery also affected the medical community. The founding of Alcoholics Anonymous (AA) in 1935 helped with this, as did federal attention to (and funding for) addiction treatment. In the 1960s, the federal government founded the National Institute on Alcohol Abuse and Alcoholism and the National Institute on Drug Abuse, which created state, local, and federal partnerships for the funding of SUD research (White, 2014). Much of this work centered on the medical model, which views SUD as a disease that fits the definition of the following characteristics:

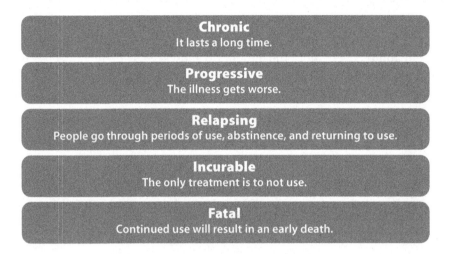

Chronic
It lasts a long time.

Progressive
The illness gets worse.

Relapsing
People go through periods of use, abstinence, and returning to use.

Incurable
The only treatment is to not use.

Fatal
Continued use will result in an early death.

The medical model stands in contrast to the moral model in that it views people with SUD as being ill—not as having a character defect. Continuing research into the impact of SUD on the brain and the potential genetic aspects of SUD provide support for this theory. The medical model has also helped to destigmatize SUD and led to more effective (and humane) treatments.

Psychodynamic Model

The psychodynamic model maintains that a person's drug use is due to underlying problems that they may not be aware of. By identifying these underlying issues and resolving them, the individual will be less likely to continue their use (West, 2012). The self-medication hypothesis of drug use, which holds that people use substances to medicate unrecognized mental health problems, is predicated on the psychodynamic model. Our use of defense mechanisms to deny or minimize SUD is also grounded in this model.

The psychodynamic model's focus on underlying issues helps us understand the ways that trauma, particularly childhood trauma and neglect, are linked to SUD. For example, I was recently in a meeting with a peer recovery specialist (an individual with lived experience of SUD and mental health issues) who worked in a harm reduction setting. I'll paraphrase some of what he said, which mirrors other things I've heard other people say on the topic of trauma and SUD:

I was told for years that I had a disease that caused me to use drugs and that the way to deal with this disease was to not use. Through a lot of counseling and hard work, I've come to recognize that my SUD was a symptom of my trauma history. I honestly believe that had I not experienced my traumas, I would not have developed a SUD. When I used to say this in treatment, I was told I was in denial of my "real" problem or that I was "rationalizing my behaviors." The thing is, I wasn't! In order to truly get well (in recovery), I had to not only address the symptoms of what was wrong with me—in other words, my drug use—but I also had to deal with the root cause: my trauma. This was not an either/or approach but a holistic approach to address symptoms and the root causes. I honestly believe that doing this has kept me alive.

Behavioral Reinforcement Model

The behavioral reinforcement model takes a contrasting view of SUD from the psychodynamic model in that it places the focus outside the person. Rather than emphasizing an individual's internal drives or past trauma, the reinforcement model maintains that a client's environment and the reinforcing effects of the substance are the primary motivators for SUD or recovery. According to this model, it is important to consider the effects of both positive and negative reinforcement (Inaba & Cohen, 2014):

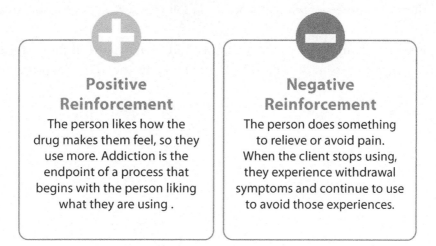

Treatment involves helping the client understand how these reinforcement systems work and then replacing drugs with other things (West, 2012).

Stress-Diathesis Model

The stress-diathesis model brings together parts of the medical, psychodynamic, and behavioral reinforcement models. This model has perhaps the best explanation for the role trauma plays in the lives of people with SUD. According to the model, a genetic predisposition to addiction (*diathesis*) in combination with environmental influences (*stress*) increases the likelihood that someone will develop a SUD. The stronger the diathesis, the fewer drugs are needed to move the person into SUD.

Like the other theories we have examined, the stress-diathesis theory holds that SUD is a process that often encompasses a person's life. By helping a client to understand their diathesis and identify (and manage) their stressors, they can more easily move toward recovery (Inaba & Cohen, 2014).

WHICH THEORY SHOULD I USE?

A review of the previous theories generates a common question: Which theory should I use? Remember that these are theories, neither proven nor disproved. Each is studied, challenged, and modified as new information becomes available. These theories are also not mutually exclusive; many are compatible with one another. It is possible to use one theory to explain how some people develop SUD and another theory to explain how others develop SUD. This is an eclectic and accepted approach. Therefore, to answer the question of which theory to use—any and all of them! Regardless of which theories you follow, they should support treatment approaches for SUD.

Let's examine three case examples of people living with SUD. As you read these stories, consider which theories might explain why the person developed SUD and how this theoretical approach might inform their treatment approaches.

Case Study #1: Denny

Denny grew up in an upper-middle class neighborhood. Both of his grandfathers, paternal and maternal, were alcoholics—one entered recovery in middle age, and the other died in his 50s from medical problems due to alcohol use. Because Denny's parents grew up living with self-described alcoholics, they rarely drank. Denny reported that his parents clearly loved one another and him.

Denny got good grades in middle school and played several sports. During this time, some of his teammates introduced him to alcohol, and Denny found that he liked getting drunk. In high school, he discovered marijuana and cocaine, as the school's population was affluent and drugs were readily available. Denny soon left sports behind, and his grades dropped. Denny's parents took him to counseling, which he found amusing but unhelpful.

Denny was first arrested for marijuana possession when he was a senior in high school and was placed on probation. Because of his county's zero-tolerance policy toward substance use, he was expelled from school, even though he had not been caught with marijuana on school property. Denny had a difficult time on probation, mainly because he kept testing positive for cannabis on his urine drug screens. Eventually, the judge gave Denny a choice: jail or a residential program. Because Denny's parents had the means (and did not want him to go to jail), the obvious choice was residential treatment.

Denny stayed in the program for six months, earning his general equivalency diploma and enrolling in community college courses. During this time, his parents became involved in a group that ministered to families with members who have struggled with SUD. Denny's parents found the group to be nonjudgmental, and they helped them learn how to love Denny without enabling him. When Denny finished treatment, he went to live in a recovery house and continued to do well for about a year.

After Denny left the recovery house, he remained involved in the 12-step community, but after several months, his parents became concerned that he seemed to be pulling away from them. Shortly thereafter, Denny dropped off their radar. They later learned that he had discovered heroin. For the last two years of his life, Denny struggled with heroin use. This included short stays in psychiatric hospitals for detoxification and several placements in treatment programs. Once Denny was discharged from each program, he often resumed using. His family remained concerned and continued to help him get treatment, but they did not give him money or allow him to stay in their home when he was using heroin.

Early one morning, Denny passed out after injecting himself with heroin. The people he was living with, who also use heroin, could not revive him. He was 23.

What were some causative factors for Denny's SUD?

Which theories explain how his SUD developed? Why?

How would you have intervened with Denny?

Case Study #2: Ashley

I met Ashley in the emergency department where I worked. She was 23 years old and scared. She said that she needed help and asked to speak with a counselor. In speaking with her, Ashley described growing up in public housing and never knowing her father. She remembers sitting at the top of the stairs of her family's tiny apartment when she was 4 years old, listening to her mother "entertain" men downstairs, while trying to keep her 2-year-old brother quiet.

"I knew what crack smelled like then," she told me.

Throughout her childhood, Ashley witnessed her mother assaulted many times. Ashley was also molested by an uncle when she was 7 and was raped by her mother's boyfriend when she was 12. When Ashley told her mother about it, her mother hit her.

Ashley was never encouraged to attend school, and she found many of her teachers to be overworked and apathetic. She discovered marijuana when she was 12 years old, which she said made her feel good and forget her feelings of emptiness. She experimented with pills in her early teens before discovering heroin at age 19.

Ashley loved how heroin made her feel like she could do anything. At first, she snorted heroin powder and later moved on to intravenous heroin. Before long, she was prostituting to support her habit. At this point, Ashley no longer enjoyed heroin and only used it to avoid feeling sick. She was jailed several times for prostitution and possession of heroin but was never offered substance use treatment. Whenever she was incarcerated, she became violently ill from opioid withdrawal.

Ashley came to the emergency department that afternoon after escaping from three older men who had kept her plied with heroin while they raped her in an abandoned house. The hospital social worker and I worked to arrange shelter and SUD treatment for her.

What were some causative factors for Ashely's SUD?

Which theories explain how SUD developed for Ashley? Why?

How would you have intervened with Ashley?

Case Study #3: Fatima

Fatima was 44 years old, divorced, and a mother of two college-aged children. She never used substances, apart from an occasional glass of wine. She reported that her upbringing was "normal" and denied any abuse or neglect. She did not have any mental health issues.

Years ago, when Fatima was walking outside the bank where she worked, she slipped on an icy sidewalk and fell off a curb onto her back. While she did not break any bones, her back was injured, requiring rest. Fatima was in a lot of pain, so she went to her primary care physician, who prescribed her OxyContin®. Fatima was very pleased with how the medication lessened her pain.

At the time of the prescription, Fatima's doctor told her that he'd received information from the drug company and the American Medical Association stating that pain was being undertreated in the United States. He wanted Fatima to control her pain with OxyContin, so over the next few years, Fatima's dose was increased each time she developed tolerance to the medication.

Fatima was surprised one day when her doctor told her that he was concerned about her use of OxyContin. He told Fatima that he had been researching pain management and was concerned about the overuse of powerful opioid medications. He created a plan to slowly wean Fatima off the medication.

Over the following weeks, Fatima found it difficult to stick with the plan, as she felt sick when she did not have enough medication. With less medication being prescribed, she ran out of medication before her next doctor's visit and began going to other prescribers seeking more medication. At first, she was successful, but over time, she began to get turned away from other providers after her state introduced a prescription monitoring system. Fatima's primary care doctor eventually stopped prescribing her medication after he found out that she had been "doctor shopping."

Without prescriptions, Fatima felt stuck. She mentioned this to a friend who said that she knew someone who could sell her OxyContin without a prescription, so Fatima started purchasing it on the street for $1 per milligram. As her tolerance increased, Fatima found herself spending a lot of money to purchase OxyContin. She mentioned this expense one day to her dealer (for lack of a better word), and he asked her if she had ever tried heroin. Fatima was reluctant to consider this until her dealer noted the many similarities between prescription opioids and heroin. Fatima's fears were further allayed when she learned that she could snort heroin instead of having to inject. Eventually, snorting heroin became less effective, and Fatima learned how to inject herself with heroin. She used heroin in this manner for six years before trying medication for opioid use disorder.

What were some causative factors for Fatima's SUD?

Which theories explain how SUD developed for Fatima? Why?

How would you have intervened with Fatima?

RECOVERY DEFINED

While it is important to acknowledge the millions of people living with SUD, the millions who have died from SUD, and the countless people who are impacted by another person's SUD, we need to remember that there are millions of people living in recovery. Therefore, as we learn about SUD, we should pay equal attention to recovery, which is defined as follows:

> A lived experience of improved life quality and a sense of empowerment; the principles of recovery focus on the central ideas of hope, choice, freedom, and aspiration that are experienced rather than diagnosed and occur in real life settings rather than in the rarefied atmosphere of clinical settings. Recovery is a process rather than an end state, with the goal of being in an ongoing quest for a better life. (Best & Laudet, 2010, as cited in Morgan, 2019, p. 191)

In my view, an even better definition of recovery is "any positive change" (Szalavitz, 2021). Recovery is real (and possible) with SUD, and our role as practitioners is to help others address their SUD and move into recovery. We also need to remember that recovery means something different to each person; our clients define what recovery means to them. This is how we face the SUD crisis—not by fighting a war on drugs, but by joining people and walking with them in recovery.

What Is Recovery?

Recovery, like SUD, is unique for each person. Understanding what recovery is can give you (and the people working with you) an idea of where you want to be and the steps you will need to take to get there. Use the following questions to consider what recovery means to you and how you think other people view it.

Which words, names, or thoughts come to your mind when you hear the word *recovery*? (Write down as many things as you can without stopping to think about your answers.)

Draw a picture of recovery.

How would you define recovery in terms of yourself? (It is okay if you are not sure.)

ANSWERS TO *TEST YOUR KNOWLEDGE OF SUD*

1. Caffeine

2. Nicotine/tobacco

3. Alcohol

4. (1) Inhale through the mouth, (2) swallow, (3) snort through the nose, (4) inject into a vein, (5) inject into a muscle, (6) inject under the skin, (7) dissolve sublingually (absorb under the tongue), (8) absorb through the gums, (9) absorb transdermally (through the skin), (10) insert vaginally, (11) insert rectally, (12) drop into the eyeball with a dropper

5. Inhaling through the mouth

6. Alcohol withdrawal seizure, especially delirium tremens

7. The use of heroin and cocaine at the same time (e.g., injecting or snorting them together)

8. Naloxone/Narcan®

9. False: They're the same chemical with different routes of use.

10. False: The opioid crisis began much earlier than 2014, but this is when we first started seeing a lot of fentanyl in the drug supply.

11. False: Insufflation used to be safer, but fentanyl has changed this.

12. False: Point-of-care urine drug screens have a limited number of substances they can detect.

13. True: People with moderate to severe alcohol use disorders who suddenly stop drinking are at risk of developing life-threatening withdrawal seizures or delirium. People with opioid use disorder may experience extremely uncomfortable symptoms, but these are rarely fatal.

14. False: Less than half of babies born to mothers who use heroin or other opioids will experience NOWS.

15. False: This is a judgmental, outdated attitude toward recovery.

16. False: Regular use of cannabis can be harmful, especially when used heavily by adolescents and young adults.

2

The Science Behind
Substance Use Disorders

THE BIOPSYCHOSOCIAL-SPIRITUAL ASPECTS OF SUBSTANCE USE DISORDERS

Substance use disorders involve more than just drug use. They involve the *entire* person, so to address SUD, we need to understand individuals from a biological, psychological, social, and spiritual perspective.

From a **biological** perspective, it is important to understand how genetics play a role in addiction. As discussed in the previous chapter, it is common for people with a genetic predisposition to addiction to develop a SUD. We can see this in the case of identical twins adopted by different families at birth—many develop addictive or abstinent patterns consistent with their biological parents, regardless of their upbringing. Although there is not a specific, identified "addiction gene," there does appear to be many variations of genetic differences that could account for SUD in some people. Continuing research has found a shortage of dopamine receptor sites in the brains of some people with alcohol use disorder. However, as I mentioned before, SUD likely includes aspects of the individual that are due to nature (biology) *and* nurture (experiences).

We also need to consider how substances impact people on a cellular and molecular level, including the various bodily systems (e.g., pulmonary, circulatory, gastrointestinal, neurological, etc.) that are affected both during intoxication and withdrawal. When digging deeper into the neurological effects, we must remember that we are only beginning to understand the complexity of the human brain. The closer we look at the brain, the more we learn that we are just scratching the surface. For example, when I was in grade school, I was taught that we only use about 15 percent of our brains, although we now know that we actually use 100 percent. Similarly, when I was in graduate school, I was taught that once the brain was damaged, it could never heal. We now know this to be false as well, given the brain's innate capacity for neuroplasticity. We are also learning that the brain can be functionally damaged by a person's experiences, even in the absence of physical injury. This evidence is both promising and problematic for SUD treatment. It is promising in that brains that have been damaged by substance use can heal given time and the right support. It is problematic when we consider the often-harrowing experiences that people with SUD have endured before, during, and after their substance use. This range of experiences can vary across classifications, from physical traumatic brain injuries to emotional trauma—all damaging the brain in some way; this is an area where the biological and psychological meet.

When we look at the **psychological** aspects of substance use, we consider a person's underlying mental health and trauma history, including how they view themselves and how they process and learn information. This perspective allows us to better understand the intersection between mental illness and SUD, as the two often co-occur, with some people using substances to self-medicate their mental health symptoms and others developing mental illnesses because of SUD. In addition, the psychological perspective considers how many personality factors can increase the risk of SUD. Although the following is not a complete list of these factors—and they may not apply to everyone—these are not uncommon in people who develop SUD.

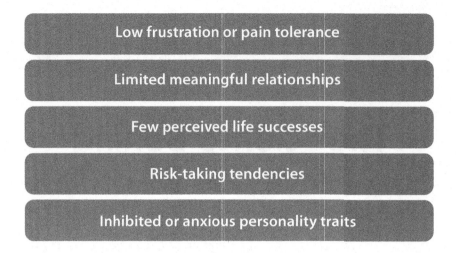

Given that we are social creatures, meant to live in community, we must also take a **social** approach to understanding SUD, which considers our relationships with the people close to us and our relationship with humanity (and the environment) in general. The attitudes of those around us regarding substances will influence our actions just as our attitudes and actions impact theirs. Likewise, a person's SUD impacts their family, employment, academics, financial well-being, and many other things that affect the people around them. In fact, there is evidence that the broader environment plays as much of a part in contributing to SUD as biology. Examples of environmental factors that are major risk factors for SUD include economic hardship, availability of drugs in the community, unstable living conditions, lack of access to nutrition, and lack of access to treatment. Therefore, providing quality SUD treatment involves acting within our communities to ensure that treatment is accessible, that clients have other resources available to them, and that reintegration into society (e.g., employment, academics, etc.) is included as part of recovery. Treatment should also involve the family as individuals with SUD seek to repair relationships (and form healthy relationships) in their lives.

Finally, although **spirituality** is often not connected to the biopsychosocial perspective, I believe it must be considered in our view of SUD. As clinicians, we are often reluctant to discuss spirituality because we want to be mindful about imposing our beliefs onto our clients, but this reluctance can lead us to miss an important part of the people we work with. Spirituality involves the recognition that we are all connected to something greater than us. What we identify as this "something" is the essence of our spirituality. Spirituality seeks to answer life's biggest questions: Why are we here? Why do we have to die? Why does pain exist in the world? For many people, their religious beliefs inform how they experience spirituality, but many people find meaning outside of religion, so it is important that we respect the beliefs (or absence of beliefs) of our clients.

When considering the role of SUD on spirituality, we must understand that substance use can impact an individual's spirituality by making them feel unworthy and useless. People don't usually consider thoughts of something greater than themselves when they are swallowed up in self-loathing. In addition, the trauma associated with spiritual abuse, which involves harm afflicted to someone in the name of a religion or deity, can lead someone to develop a SUD. However, spirituality can be a positive part of recovery. When people have an appreciation that there are things greater than themselves, it can be a source of strength and provide meaning for their recovery or their life as a whole. Furthermore, spiritual practices can promote community formation and a source of support for people in recovery.

Biopsychosocial-Spiritual
Case Study: Aaron

Aaron was a 15-year-old male in a juvenile drug treatment court where I was a clinician. He had been charged with possession of marijuana, public intoxication, petty larceny, and several probation violations. If he completed the program, his charges would be dismissed.

I met with Aaron soon after he started the program, just prior to his release from detention to his mother's care. He stated that he accepted the plea to enter drug court because he wanted to enter the Army when he turned 18 and needed a clean record. Although he reported having several "shrinks" in the past, some who were nice, they did not help him. He was nonetheless willing to talk with me because "I know it's your job."

The man who Aaron knew as his father died of cancer when Aaron was 12. Aaron skipped school for several months to visit his dad in the hospital as he was dying. During this time, Aaron's older brother found out that their dad was not their biological father. Aaron's brother, who regularly used drugs and alcohol, became drunk one night and told Aaron about this news.

This devastated Aaron. He confronted his mother about it, and she said that the information was true. Aaron's biological father had abandoned the family prior to Aaron's birth. Shortly after this, she met and married the man Aaron considered his father, who subsequently raised the boys as his own. Aaron learned that his biological father died from complications related to alcoholism five years earlier.

"So, see if this makes sense," said Aaron, sitting across a table from me. "My dad dies, but he's not really my dad. I mean how fucked up is that? Two dads dead."

I paused. "I'm sorry. I know that doesn't sound like much, but I am sorry."

Aaron remained silent.

"Is that when you started to use?" I asked.

"Hell no," said Aaron. "I smoked weed for the first time when I was eight. I was also drinking and smoking cigarettes at that time. When my dad died, I started smoking more. I just didn't care about anything. I stopped going to school, not that school ever did anything for me, ya know? I would go to school, but that was so I could sell my Adderall® to the smart kids. Those geeks were so worried about getting good grades, they loved taking that stuff. I'd then use the money and buy weed. I'd get enough to smoke every day."

"At no cost to you?"

"Yep, pretty good deal; everyone wins."

"Except you were expelled in the ninth grade, without ever earning a single credit."

"School is stupid," he replied. "I can pass the GED on the first try."

Aaron continued on to say that he planned to do whatever he needed to in the drug court program to get through it in the minimum time of one year. He did not plan to stop his use of drugs for the long term, just long enough to get through the program.

What are some biological factors that could be impacting Aaron's SUD?

What else would you like to know about Aaron's biological makeup? How would you get this information?

What are some psychological factors that could be impacting Aaron's SUD?

What else would you like to know about Aaron's psychological functioning? How would you get this information?

What are some social factors that could be impacting Aaron's SUD?

What else would you like to know about Aaron's social environment? How would you get this information?

What are some spiritual factors that could be impacting Aaron's SUD?

What else would you like to know about Aaron's spirituality? How would you get this information?

Understanding the Biopsychosocial-Spiritual Aspects of Your SUD

Substance use impacts every aspect of your life. Understanding the many ways you have been affected by substances can help you plan how to begin and sustain recovery. Use the following questions to help you understand how you have been affected by your SUD.

Biological

How has your drug use impacted each of the following areas in your body?

Neurological (e.g., memory problems, inability to concentrate)

Circulatory (e.g., numbness in hands or feet, chest pains, hypertension)

Respiratory (e.g., shortness of breath, coughing)

Reproductive (e.g., erectile dysfunction, loss of interest in sex)

Gastrointestinal (e.g., abdominal pains, nausea, weight loss or gain)

Dental (e.g., tooth loss, gum recession)

Dermatological (e.g., burns, unhealthy skin)

Immune (e.g., frequent illness)

What are some biological problems you have that make you want to continue using drugs?

What could change with your biological systems if you stopped or reduced your drug use?

Psychological

How has your drug use changed how you think about yourself?

How has your drug use changed how you think about others?

How has your drug use changed how you think about the world?

Were you diagnosed with a mental illness prior to your SUD? If so, how has your SUD impacted your mental health symptoms?

Some people use substances to self-medicate. Do you think you have done this? How?

Social

How does your living environment contribute to your drug use?

How does your living environment contribute to your recovery?

What were your family's attitudes about drugs when you were growing up?

What are the attitudes or beliefs about drugs among the people you live with now?

What opportunities for recovery are available in your community?

Spiritual

What are your spiritual beliefs?

How has your SUD impacted your spiritual beliefs?

How could spirituality help you in recovery?

TRAUMA AND SUBSTANCE USE

Several years ago, when I helped start a medication-assisted treatment program for adults with opioid use disorder, my colleagues and I quickly realized how intertwined trauma was in our clients' SUD. For many of our clients, their trauma had been dismissed or ignored by previous SUD treatment providers, propelling them further into their SUD and away from treatment. We concluded we could not treat their SUD without concurrently treating their trauma. According to the American Psychological Association, trauma is defined as follows:

> Any disturbing experience that results in significant fear, helplessness, dissociation, confusion, or other disruptive feelings intense enough to have a long-lasting negative impact on a person's attitudes, behavior, and other aspects of functioning. Traumatic events include those caused by human behavior (e.g., rape, toxic accidents) as well as by nature (e.g., earthquakes) and often challenge an individual's view of the world as a just, safe, and predictable place. (American Psychological Association, 2013, p. 597)

Although trauma can have lasting impacts at any stage of development, we now know that traumatic childhood experiences in particular can lead to adverse health outcomes in later life, including SUD (Levine, 2015; Maté, 2010; van der Kolk, 2014). Understanding these adverse childhood experiences, or ACEs as they are more commonly known, can help clients understand how their early experiences impact them as adults. We also need to understand some of the ways that people can be traumatized and the symptoms that may follow. For instance, traumatic events can be triggers for substance use. However, clients should understand that *exposure* to trauma does not necessarily mean they will experience lasting trauma symptoms. The following pages can help clients examine their own trauma, along with its history and related triggers. It is important that this worksheet be used in session and that this material only be used if the client feels comfortable doing so.

Trauma and Its Symptoms

Examples of Trauma	
Chronic medical issues	Medical issues of a primary caretaker of a family member
Deployment into a combat zone; operating remote-controlled drones in combat operations	Multiple relocations
	Natural or human-made disaster
Family member's incarceration	Political refugee
Family member's substance use	Unstable housing
Family member's sudden death (particularly suicide or homicide)	Verbal, physical, or sexual abuse
Incarceration or long-term admission to a psychiatric facility	Witness of parental violence; parental separation or divorce

Trauma Symptoms	
Anger, irritability	Intrusive thoughts
Avoidance of reminders of the trauma	Memory problems
Dissociation	Mood swings
Exaggerated startle response	Nightmares
Fear, anxiety, depression	Sleep problems
Guilt, shame	Shock, disbelief
Hypervigilance	Withdrawal from others

How Trauma May Trigger Your Use

The connection between trauma and substance use is substantial for many people. Given that people experience trauma in different ways, understanding your own experiences with stressful or traumatic events can help you understand your SUD. Use the following questions to help you understand trauma as it relates to your SUD.

How would you define trauma?

What are some examples of trauma (not necessarily things you've experienced)?

Have you experienced any events that you consider to be traumatic? If so, what?

Have you struggled with any trauma symptoms as a result of this event? For example, do you experience nightmares, flashbacks, or difficulty concentrating? Do you find yourself constantly on edge or emotionally numb?

If you still experience trauma symptoms, what are some things you do to cope?

Do you use substances to help you cope? If so, which ones?

How do these substances alleviate your trauma symptoms? How do they make them worse?

Are there any alternative coping strategies you could use in response to your traumatic symptoms? If so, which ones?

OUR RESPONSE TO TRAUMA

In order to understand the science behind addiction as it relates to trauma, it is important to know how our bodies are wired to respond to potential threats in our environment. As humans, we all have a built-in stress response system that has kept our species alive for hundreds of thousands of years. This system primes us with the ability to identify and hyperfocus on real or perceived threats in our environment so we can react accordingly when faced with those threats. Humans have few natural defenses except to run away. Until we developed basic tools and learned to live in groups for mutual protection, our only hope to avoid these threats was to run a little faster than the slowest person in our group.

Much of this stress response is governed by the mesolimbic system, located in the mid-brain. The mesolimbic system sits on top of the brain stem and the pons, which control our body's essential life functions. When activated by a threat, the mesolimbic system quickly reads the situation and sends a signal for the body to respond in several ways, to either get away from the threat or prepare to take the threat on. While we may become aware of this process in our prefrontal cortex—which is the seat of consciousness and executive functioning—that realization happens much slower than the time in which it takes in the mesolimbic system to act—which is why our body may take action before our minds process why we are taking said action.

Most of the time, when we are confronted with a threat, we respond and then return to a baseline state of "normalcy." However, trauma events appear to interfere with our ability to return to baseline, causing some people—particularly those who experienced trauma, neglect, or a lack of attachment at a young age—to remain stuck in the trauma long after the traumatic event has ended (Friesen et al., 2013). In other words, their mesolimbic system remains on high alert, and even minor or unrelated events can retrigger the system.

Levels of Safety

There are five primary ways that people respond to stress, including traumatic events, to regain a sense of safety: They may attempt to engage with others, to flee the situation, to fight back, to freeze, or to fawn. Most of the time, we move through these events sequentially as we attempt to neutralize the threat and return to a state of normalcy. However, it is possible for people to experience these reactions out of sequence, particularly people with SUD, who may gravitate toward the freeze response because it shares similarities with inebriation.

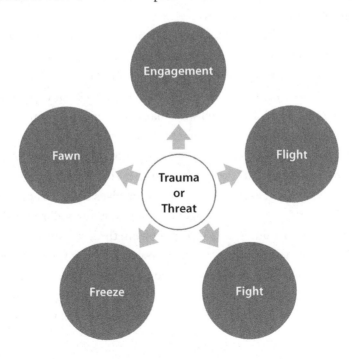

The first way we usually try to deal with a threat is to **engage** with others, especially with people we hope will be supportive. For example, a few years ago, as I was flying home following a teaching tour, the young woman seated next to me started talking to me in a very rapid and hurried manner. I had noticed something similar happen on an earlier flight with a passenger sitting in front of me, and in both situations, I guessed that the person was nervous about flying. This time, however, I decided to test my hunch.

"I couldn't help but notice that as we started to back away from the gate, you started talking faster. It's not a problem, but I'm curious: Are you nervous about flying?" I asked.

"Wow!" she exclaimed. "How did you know?"

"Well," I said, sitting back in my seat and straightening my tie, "I'm a therapist and we just know these things…"

Actually, I didn't really say that. I instead explained that I had just finished teaching a class to professionals about high-risk clients, including people with trauma. I summarized how our brains can respond to real or perceived threats and explained that whether she realized it or not, she was tapping into our hardwired need for engagement by turning to me—a stranger—for support.

I wonder how often we connect with others when we feel stressed or traumatized and we simply do not realize it. More importantly, what if there is no one present to engage with? Even worse, what if the people we attempt to engage try to hurt us further? When engagement fails, we progress to the next step in the sequence by trying to get away from the threat, a process called **flight**. As I mentioned in the introduction to this book, one of the first places I worked in the clinical field was in a residential program for "emotionally disturbed" adolescents, many of whom we would now recognize as having posttraumatic stress disorder (PTSD). We noticed that when these adolescents were faced with stressful events, some of which undoubtedly reminded them of their abusive histories, many tried to leave the cottage. Quite often, they were not trying to completely run away from campus; they simply wanted time to escape the stressful situation and calm down.

But what if a person cannot get away from the source of their stress? In these cases, we often turn to **fight**. In the residential treatment program, I eventually became a counselor for a group of around 10 males. Some of these clients became violent with little provocation, but with the benefit of hindsight, I can see now that they often resorted to fighting because they couldn't flee someone or something that they viewed as threatening. Many times, I was hit or kicked because my efforts to be helpful or engage the young person were seen as a threat. When I did not get out of the way or move quickly enough, I was assaulted. In retrospect, the best course of action would have been to let them flee—and simply get out of their way.

Now, if the person we are trying to fight is too strong for us, we often move to the next step of the stress response sequence and **freeze**. We can see this response in animals who feign death in response to a predator. In humans, freezing can manifest in different ways. Some people will hold completely still, and others may pretend they are asleep. Still others will dissociate, feeling numb, outside their body, or experiencing a sense that what is happening is not real. Given that the "high" associated with many substances can mimic the freeze reaction, many clients I worked with often resorted to this state when faced with a triggering situation. Especially for those with significant trauma histories, being in a freeze state became normal to them. When not in this state, they became anxious, confused, and very uncomfortable. Substances helped them to either re-enter or maintain this state.

The last trauma response we will examine is **fawning**, which involves trying to appease the source of the threat in order to avoid conflict (Walker, 2014). Whereas engagement, flight, fight, and freeze all reflect *reactive* response to a threat, fawning can also be a *proactive* attempt to forestall future threats from someone who has demonstrated past danger. When people fawn, they do everything in their power to please the other person—at the expense of their own needs and desires—because they believe that avoiding future trauma is in their best interest. Oftentimes, substance use can help individuals be more comfortable with fawning by making them numb them to the situation. The person who is a threat may also use substances to keep the person who is fawning in their subservient state.

Several clients I have worked with have demonstrated fawning by obeying every request of their partner in order to avoid upsetting them. In some of those cases, the partner was also the primary source of the clients' drugs, so forestalling violence also served to maintain their access to the substances they were dependent on.

Levels of Safety Response

When humans are faced with a threat, whether real or perceived, we instinctively react in one of five ways: by engaging, fleeing, fighting, freezing, or fawning. These reactions can continue even when the threat is over, making it difficult to move on and causing us to feel like we are stuck in the past. Sometimes this can lead us to engage in unhelpful behaviors that carry their own difficulties, such as substance use. Use the following questions to consider the ways you have reacted to stressful or traumatic events.

Engagement: Reaching out to others for connection and support when you feel stressed or threatened

How have you turned to other people when you felt stressed or threatened?

What was happening that caused you to turn to others for support?

With whom did you engage?

What did you do if you were unable to connect with someone safe and supportive?

Flight: Escaping from the threat by running away

What kind of threats have you tried to get away from?

How have you tried to escape from these threats?

What did you do if you couldn't get away?

Fight: Taking action against the threat by fighting back

In what types of stressful or traumatic situations have you tried to fight back?

How did you fight?

Why did you fight?

What did you do if you couldn't overcome the threat?

Freeze: Going into state of shock, numbness, immobility, or depersonalization when the threat feels overwhelming or inescapable

What kinds of situations have caused you to exhibit the freeze response?

What does the freeze response look like for you? How do you experience it?

How have substances helped you engage in the freeze response?

Fawn: Responding to a threat by trying to appease the attacker

Are there any times when you have tried to cope with an abusive or traumatic situation by engaging in fawning behavior?

Toward whom did you engage the fawn response?

Which parts of yourself did you have to hide in order to please this other person?

NEUROBIOLOGY OF SUD

A basic understanding of how substances impact the brain is important in treating people with SUD. An addictive drug refers to any substance that stimulates the limbic system, but there are three general rules in psychopharmacology that apply to all drugs:

1. All drugs act by changing the rate of what is already going on.

2. All drugs have side effects.

3. The brain adapts to all drugs that affect it by counteracting the drug's effects.

The brain's response to a drug is always to facilitate the opposite state, so the only way for any person who regularly uses to feel normal is to take the drug (Grisel, 2019). Our brains are hardwired to want to stay in balance, a process called *homeostasis*. For example, when a person takes a stimulant, their brain will try to move them toward homeostasis by slowing them down. This can involve decreasing the number of receptor sites of neurotransmitters impacted by stimulant use or increasing the actions of neurotransmitters that slow down the brain. The person will be able to feel this slowness and, in response, takes more of the stimulant to "feel normal." This back-and-forth process repeats itself many times throughout each day.

How Drugs Get to the Brain

Substances interact with the brain (and body) in complex ways. Whereas **pharmacodynamics** is the study of a drug's effect on the body, **pharmacokinetics** is the study of the body's effect on a drug—that is, how a drug is absorbed, distributed, metabolized, eliminated, and excreted by the body. These processes are influenced by the manner in which the substance is administered into the body, its speed of transit to the brain, the rate at which it is metabolized and eliminated, and how well a specific substance "fits" with its target neurotransmitter (Inaba & Cohen, 2014).

In all methods of administration, the person using will begin to feel the effects of the substance when it reaches the brain. The more rapidly a drug reaches this target, the greater its reinforcing potential (i.e., the person's desire to continue using the substance) will be. The following table lists the different routes of use, noting the time it takes to reach the brain, in quickest to slowest order (Inaba & Cohen, 2014).

Method	Time to Reach the Brain
Inhalation through the mouth: Inhalation is the quickest way to the brain.	7–10 seconds
Injection: Injection is the most dangerous method, as it bypasses the body's natural defenses and increases the risk of exposure to blood-borne infections. It can involve any of the following methods: • Intravenous injection • Intramuscular injection • Subcutaneous injection	15–30 seconds 3–5 minutes 3–5 minutes
Mucous membrane absorption: Mucous membrane absorption can involve any of the following methods: • Insufflation (snorting through the nose) • Sublingually (dissolving under the tongue) • Buccally (dissolving between the gums and cheek) • Rectally • Vaginally • Through the eyeball (using an eyedropper)	10–15 minutes
Oral ingestion: Oral ingestion occurs when the drug is absorbed by the stomach or small intestine.	20–30 minutes
Contact absorption: Contact absorption occurs through the skin, with the effects lasting up to 7 days. (The slow action of contact absorption means that this is not a method in which people use substances to achieve intoxication.)	Up to 2 days to reach full effect

Pathways to the Brain

When substances reach the bloodstream, the drug will be distributed to the rest of the body, and in just 10 to 15 seconds, the drug reaches the *blood-brain barrier*, which consists of capillaries with tightly sealed cells that allow only certain substances to pass through. This barrier exists to protect the brain, and certain substances pass through it more quickly than others. For example, heroin passes the barrier faster than morphine; this quick passage is what helps to create the high associated with heroin that is generally absent with morphine (Inaba & Cohen, 2014).

SUD and Neurotransmitters

Our brain comprises about 100 billion nerve cells. These cells are not in physical contact with one another, so they communicate by using molecules called neurotransmitters to cross the gaps between them (known as *synaptic gaps*). The nervous system uses these neurotransmitters to regulate necessary functions of the body, including aiding memory, stimulating hormones, coordinating movement, processing digestion, and many, many more. Each nerve cell produces a single type of neurotransmitter, which is then released when the cell "fires." We believe there are 60 or so neurotransmitters, but as we have yet to identify them all, there could easily be more.

While each cell produces only one neurotransmitter, cells contain multiple places for other neurotransmitters to attach to the cell, which are known as *receptor sites*. Neurotransmitters can only "dock" with specific receptor sites. For example, dopamine molecules can only dock with a dopamine receptor site, and they are unable to dock in all other types of receptor sites. If enough receptor sites are filled by these neurotransmitters, the cell fires and releases its own neurotransmitters into the synaptic gap. Some of these neurotransmitter molecules find docking sites on other cells, and the process continues. Neurotransmitters that do not find a place to dock are reabsorbed by cells to be used again, a process sometimes called reuptake.

Substances of use, including medications and other drugs, can impact this process in several ways. Most substances act like neurotransmitters and dock in receptor sites meant for neurotransmitters. We call these drugs **agonists**. Many of these substances do a better job of docking than neurotransmitters, which can cause the cell to fire with fewer receptor sites being activated. In contrast, drugs that are **antagonists** dock at the receptor site but do not cause the receptor to fire the cell. Examples include naltrexone and naloxone, which block opioid receptors and can therefore reverse opioid overdoses.

Other substances increase (or decrease) the production of neurotransmitters, and some can impact neurotransmitter reuptake. The following table provides a list of some of the neurotransmitters and how they are impacted by the use of certain substances and SUD.

ɣ-Aminobutyric acid (GABA)	This is a suppressive neurotransmitter, meaning that it blocks impulses between nerve cells, facilitates muscle relaxation, and slows down the brain. Increasing GABA decreases the actions of other neurotransmitters, while decreasing GABA increases the actions of other neurotransmitters. Benzodiazepines and other central nervous depressants cause a greater release of GABA, which slows the actions of other neurotransmitters.
Glutamate	This is an excitatory neurotransmitter, meaning that it has a simulating effect on a neuron. Glutamate is involved with learning and also enhances the effects of dopamine. Alcohol decreases glutamate, which slows the actions of other neurotransmitters.
Serotonin	This neurotransmitter regulates digestion, moods, body temperature, sleep, sexuality, and movement. Many psychedelic plants and substances increase serotonin production or block the reuptake of serotonin, leaving more of it in the synaptic gap for use.
Norepinephrine	Norepinephrine affects heart rate, digestion, fluid balance, dreaming, moods, and arousal to the environment. Many stimulants increase norepinephrine, increasing arousal and energy.
Endocannabinoids	This neurotransmitter is involved in mood management, pain control, and other neurological functions. Cannabis and synthetic cannabinoids can dock with endocannabinoid receptor sites; this often happens more effectively than natural endocannabinoids.
Dopamine	Dopamine is a key neurotransmitter associated with SUD and behavioral addictions. It is associated with motivation, basic drives, sleep, working memory, attention, movement, and pleasure or reward. Its action within the brain's reward center is a key part of the pleasurable effects of substances.
Acetylcholine	Acetylcholine is released where nerves meet muscles, tissues, and glands. Its receptors are also activated by nicotine.
Endorphins and substance P	These neurotransmitters are involved in pain regulation and sensations of dreaminess and calm. They are released during stress, relaxation, and pain. Opioids mimic these neurotransmitters and often fit more easily with opioid receptors, so they have a much stronger impact than endorphins or substance P.
Histamine	Histamine controls tissue inflammation, emotions, and sleep. It is also impacted by many substances, including alcohol and antihistamines (which people can misuse for intoxication purposes).

Reward/Control Pathways

The human brain is equipped with an internal reward system that motivates us to do things that keep us alive or continue the human species. For example, we crave sweet foods because in our evolutionary history, our brains associated sweet foods with higher energy. Maintaining this energy was important so we could run just a little faster than the next person to avoid becoming some animal's lunch. This reward system is also activated by sexual activity, thus motivating us to want to have sex and continue humanity.

Addictive substances activate this reward system and push it into overdrive. While different substances impact different neurotransmitters, dopamine and serotonin are the primary neurotransmitters involved with the reward system. The following is a basic summary of how substances stimulate our reward pathways.

The nucleus accumbens (NA), sometimes called the "go circuit," is involved with reward and reinforcement behaviors. The NA registers strong pleasurable feelings and essentially instructs the person using substances to "keep doing what you just did!" Conversely, within the cerebrum, there is a "stop circuit," which is in charge of telling you "maybe this isn't such a good idea." But when addictive substances are used regularly, the "stop circuit" is overridden by the limbic system. Substance use can also cause the "go circuit" to get flooded with dopamine and become overactive; at the same time it inhibits the "stop circuit." Long-term use of a substance can even disable the "stop circuit" completely (Inaba & Cohen, 2014). When the "go circuit" gets flooded with dopamine, the hippocampus and other parts of the limbic system lay down memories of this rapid sense of satisfaction. Memories are stored throughout the brain, but memories stored in older parts of the brain, including the limbic system, have prominence over those stored in the cerebrum.

The amygdala, in the limbic system, can also create a conditioned response. Much like the amygdala causes negative reactions to stimuli based on past trauma, it can cause positive reactions based on past pleasure. This causes a person using drugs to react with pleasure in response to stimuli associated with this feeling of intoxication (e.g., a bar or an acquaintance who mutually uses). The person not only remembers feelings of intoxication, but the stimuli associated with that feeling. It is for this reason that people in recovery talk about changing "people, places, and things" to limit their return to use. The association between conditioned stimuli and the reward system is extremely strong.

This entire process operates outside of a person's awareness, which is one of the reasons why people with SUD find it so difficult to stop using. The cerebrum is late to the party, and the limbic system is fully primed to reach for the next dose of whatever the person is using. Therefore, desisting from drug use is not as simple as telling someone to "just say no"—the activity in the reward pathways is happening at a near automatic pace. Understanding this process and identifying ways to interrupt it at various points is the goal of quality SUD treatment.

3

Substances of Use

Substances of use can be divided into the following classes:

- Alcohol and other depressants

- Stimulants

- Opioids

- Cannabinoids

- Psychedelics

- Inhalants

Each class has its own dependence liability (e.g., how addictive the substance is likely to be) and its own intoxication and withdrawal profiles. For example, stimulants, opioids, and alcohol have a greater dependence liability, making them more likely to result in SUD than the other classes of drugs. Similarly, some forms of substance withdrawal (specifically alcohol and other central nervous system depressants) may require immediate and ongoing medical attention to prevent further illness or death.

It is important for clinicians to understand the difference between various substances, including how they can affect clients on a physiological level and how to best intervene when someone is acutely intoxicated or going through withdrawal. In this chapter, I'll touch on different types of substances, their intoxication and withdrawal profiles, and the recommended courses of action for withdrawal and intoxication syndrome. However, there are thousands of plants and chemicals that people use to change how they think, feel, and act—more than I could list in a single book. Therefore, what follows are the more common chemicals that people use.

Alcohol and Other Central Nervous System Depressants

Alcohol is one of the oldest and most widely used substances. Alcohol impacts most of the body's systems, and because it is socially acceptable and legal, it is readily available in most cultures. Benzodiazepines are widely used to treat anxiety disorders and other problems, and at one time, they were the most prescribed psychiatric medications. Like alcohol, "benzos" are used for their intoxicating effects. Alcohol, benzos, and other depressants slow down (depress) the central nervous system, impacting judgment, coordination, and eventually basic bodily functions (e.g., respiration) when used in increasing amounts. Additional depressants are also described in the following table.

Common Depressants	
Alcohol	**Origin:** Ethyl alcohol (ETOH)
	Methods of use: Consumed, vaporized (pouring alcohol over dry ice and inhaling the vapors), introduced rectally
	Notes:
	• Of all U.S. hospital admissions, 25%–30% are due to current or past alcohol use disorder (Inaba & Cohen, 2014).
	• The use of alcohol enemas has been reported mainly among young people under 21 who think it will not trigger a breathalyzer. (They are wrong, by the way.)
Benzodiazepines	**Prescribed for:** Anxiety, seizures, sedation, muscle relaxant, insomnia (e.g., "Z-hypnotics" like Ambien® and Lunesta®), detoxifying people from alcohol
	Examples: Xanax® (alprazolam), Valium® (diazepam), Ativan® (lorazepam), Klonopin® (clonazepam), and Librium® (chlordiazepoxide).
	Notes:
	• Another example, Rohypnol (flunitrazepam), referred to as a "roofie," has a fast onset and is long acting, with strong effects at low doses. Often used as a date rape drug, it has been reformulated to release a blue dye when added to a liquid.

Common Depressants	
Barbiturates	**Examples:** Solfoton® (phenobarbital), Tuinal® (secobarbital), Nembutal® (pentobarbital), and Seconal® (secobarbital)
	Effects: Initially produce a stimulatory effect, followed by sedation; similar to benzodiazepines, but stronger and more sedating
	Street names: "Yellow jackets" (pentobarbital), "reds" (secobarbital)
	Notes:
	• They are infrequently seen on the street, and in most clinical settings have been replaced by benzodiazepines, though they are still used in some alcohol withdrawal management protocols.
	• They are dangerous to stop suddenly after prolonged use.
Gamma hydroxybutyric acid (GHB)	**Forms:** Clear liquid, powder, tablet, or capsule (known as a "club drug" or date rape drug)
	Effects: Euphoria, happiness, increased sexuality, and feeling of well-being; typically end within 4 hours; no after-effects that are common to other depressants
	Street names: "Georgia Home Boy," "Grievous Bodily Harm"
	Notes:
	• Dosing is extremely difficult and has a steep curve, which can lead to unintentional overdose.

Depressant Intoxication Syndrome Signs and Symptoms*		
Decreased respiration	Lowered inhibitions	Reduced coordination and speech
Depression	Memory loss	Relaxation
Drowsiness	Mild euphoria	Sedation

* Clients having problems staying awake, standing, or speaking should receive emergency medical attention.

Depressant Withdrawal Syndrome Signs and Symptoms

Anxiety rebound and agitation	High fever	Orthostatic hypotension
Cravings	Insomnia	Seizures
Delirium and hallucinations	Irritability	Sweating
Depersonalization	Malaise and weakness	Tachycardia
Depression	Nausea and vomiting	Tremors

Depressant Withdrawal Syndrome Progression*

Withdrawal symptoms begin 4–24 hours after the last drink.

In mild forms of withdrawal, the symptoms can resolve after 48 hours.

Tremulousness (i.e., shaking or trembling) is the earliest symptom, and many people with alcohol use disorder know this means they need to drink again to avoid more pronounced symptoms. This appears within hours after drinking stops and peaks in 1–2 days, but the symptom can persist for weeks.

In more severe forms, visual hallucinations can occur within 24 hours of cessation—to the client, these are real.

Between 6–48 hours after stopping alcohol use, 3%–4% of untreated clients will have a seizure.

In clients who have a seizure, 30%–40% will progress into delirium tremens if they are left untreated, which are fatal in up to 25% of people who are not treated.

Delirium tremens can precede or follow a seizure.

Repeated withdrawal episodes seem to kindle more serious withdrawal episodes.

* Clients displaying any depressant withdrawal symptoms should receive emergency medical attention.

Stimulants

Stimulants are the most widely used psychoactive substances in the world, particularly tobacco, caffeine, and nicotine. Recently, many areas have seen increases in cocaine and methamphetamine use likely due to the attention being given to the opioid crisis. Another disturbing trend is that fentanyl is being found in cocaine, methamphetamine, and other stimulants due to cross-contamination as drugs are diluted and repackaged while moving down the supply chain.

Common Stimulants	
Cocaine	**Forms:** Cocaine hydrochloride salt (powder); crack—(smokable form made by cooking cocaine hydrochloride with baking soda or sodium bicarbonate)
	Methods of use: Injected and snorted (salt); smoked (crack)
	Time to brain: 3–5 minutes (salt); 5–8 seconds (crack)
	Effects: Large rush followed by rapid crash
	Notes:
	• Of the two million people who use cocaine in the U.S., about 25% use crack.
	• Cocaine + alcohol = cocaethylene. The effect is like cocaine alone, but it lengthens the high and decreases the potency of the high. It also increases the toxicity of cocaine, especially cardiac conduction abnormalities.
Amphetamines	*Methylphenidate and Amphetamine* **Prescribed for:** ADHD
	Examples: Ritalin®, Concerta® (Methylphenidates); Adderall®, Vyvanse® (Amphetamines)
	Methods of use: Crushed and snorted, dissolved in water, injected
	Notes:
	• Students *not* diagnosed with ADHD may use these drugs to improve their concentration.

Common Stimulants	
Amphetamines (continued)	*Ephedrine and pseudoephedrine* **Method of use:** Often combined with caffeine in many types of weight loss products **Notes:** • These mild stimulants are precursors to more powerful amphetamines and methamphetamine.
Methamphetamines	**Methods of use:** Consumed orally, snorted, injected, smoked **Effects:** Two to three times stronger than amphetamines, lasts longer than amphetamines **Notes:** • There are hundreds of ways to manufacture methamphetamine; most "cooks" learn from other "cooks." • Methamphetamine production labs are environmental disasters. Most methamphetamine is now produced in "super labs" found in other countries and then shipped to the U.S.
Cathinones	**Origin:** Derived from the khat plant, which is typically grown in Africa and the Middle East **Methods of use:** Leaves chewed; leaves brewed in tea; Cathinone extracted and purified, snorted, injected **Effects:** More potent than caffeine but less powerful than cocaine
Methcathinone and Mephedrone	**Origin:** Synthetic (and stronger) forms of cathinone sold as "bath salts" (methylenedioxypyrovalerone or MDPV) **Effects:** Tolerance can build quickly; MDPV has four times the potency of methylphenidate; it has entactogenic and hallucinogenic properties and appears to precipitate psychosis more easily than other amphetamines because of its faster and stronger impact on the dopamine system (Winstock et al., 2011); effects are typical for most amphetamines, but coming down from use is very unpleasant. Most effects resolve in 3–4 hours, with milder effects lasting 6–8 hours.

Common Stimulants	
Nicotine	**Methods of use:** Smoked, smokeless tobacco, e-cigarettes **Effects:** Easily passes the blood-brain barrier; has a profound impact on every part of the body, especially the cardio-pulmonary system **Notes:** • It is extremely addictive and also the leading cause of preventable death in the U.S. • Each year, nicotine kills more people than alcohol, cocaine, and heroin combined. • Among regular smokers, 80% begin use in adolescence.
Caffeine	**Prescribed for:** Migraines, appetite suppressant **Notes:** • Caffeine is the most used psychoactive drug in the world. • Energy drinks contain high levels of caffeine and are increasingly misused by children and adolescents.

Stimulant Intoxication Syndrome Signs and Symptoms*		
Aggression	Fast heartbeat	Hypertension
Delusions and paranoia	Fever	Panic
Dilated pupils	Hyperactivity	Seizures

* People with seizures, hypertension, tachycardia, and delirium require emergency medical care, while those showing other symptoms can receive supportive care.

Stimulant Withdrawal Syndrome Signs and Symptoms		
Anhedonia	Fatigue	Irritability
Anxiety	Headaches	Paranoia
Apathy	Hypersomnia	Psychomotor retardation, then agitation
Cravings	Increased appetite	Social withdrawal
Depression	Insomnia	

Stimulant Withdrawal Progression*
The body must rest at some point, so no matter how much stimulant a person uses, they will eventually crash.
Acute withdrawal symptoms usually peak within 2–4 days, but depression, anxiety, and irritability can continue for months.
Craving often continues for months or years.
Antidepressants may be used to address withdrawal-related depressive symptoms.

* Those showing symptoms should receive supportive care.

Cocaine and Methamphetamine Differences	
Cocaine	**Methamphetamine**
Plant derived	Human-made
More intense rush	Less intense rush
Smoking or injecting produces a brief, intense high	Smoking or injecting produces a longer-lasting high
Cannot be taken orally	Can be taken orally
50% of the drug is removed from the body in 1 hour	50% of the drug is removed from the body in 12 hours

Opioids

Opioids or Opiates?

All opiates (substances derived from the opium poppy plant: morphine, codeine, and heroin) are opioids, but not all opioids are opiates. Opioids, many of which are synthetic or semi-synthetic chemicals (e.g., oxycodone, fentanyl, methadone, buprenorphine), is a term used to describe any substance that will bind to the opioid receptor sites in cells.

Common Opioids[*]	
Opium	**Origin:** Derived from poppy plants, which are typically grown in South Asia and Central America **Notes:** • It takes 10 kg of opium to make 1 kg of morphine. • Opium alkaloids—include primarily morphine, codeine, and thebaine.
Heroin (diacetylmorphine/ diamorphine)	**Forms:** Lower grade (#3) and higher grade (#4), which is up to 90% pure **Methods of use:** Injected intravenously, injected intramuscularly, or skin-popped (#3); insufflated, smoked, injected (#4) **Time to brain:** 10–15 seconds (insufflation, smoked); 20 seconds (intravenous injection); 5–8 minutes (muscular injection) **Effects:** A rush, including feelings of warmth and pleasure, followed by a lengthy period of sedation (known as "nodding out"); decreases respiration (leading cause of overdose deaths) **Street names:** "Dope," "junk," "smack," "horse," "H," "shit," "scramble," "cheese," "tar," "brown sugar," "black tar" (#3), "China White" (#4) **Notes:** • Heroin is one to four times the strength of morphine and crosses the blood-brain barrier quicker than morphine. • Overdose potential is high; these are typically accidental. • A "speedball" involves simultaneously injecting/insufflating heroin and cocaine, which extends the high from both drugs.

[*] Methadone and buprenorphine will be covered in the pharmacotherapy section.

Common Opioids	
Morphine	**Methods of use:** Injected, consumed, applied sublingually, taken as a suppository **Examples:** MS-Contin®, Oramorph SR®, MSIR®, Roxanol®, Kadian®, RMD®
Codeine	**Origin:** Derived from opium **Prescribed as:** Cough suppressant **Effects:** 15% the strength of morphine
Fentanyl	**Origin:** Most illicit fentanyl is manufactured in China and India and smuggled into the United States (Westhoff, 2019) **Forms:** Thousands of fentanyl analogues, including acetyl fentanyl, sufentanil, and carfentanil; sometimes sold in gelatin capsules ("beans") to people who prefer fentanyl to heroin **Prescribed as:** Pain management **Notes:** • Most forms of fentanyl have been found in seized drug products in every state in the United States.
Kratom (Mitragyna speciosa)	**Origin:** Kratom, an herb that grows into tree-like plants that are typically grown in Southeast Asia **Methods of use:** Raw leaves are eaten or brewed into a tea; dried leaves are crushed and put into capsules **Effects:** Dose-sensitive and highly variable, with mild/pleasant stimulation at lose doses and sedating, stupor-inducing effects at extremely high doses **Notes:** • It is legal in many states and has a heavy internet sales presence.
Hydrocodone	**Examples:** Vicodin®, Lortab®, Norco® **Effects:** It has about 60% the strength of morphine. **Notes:** • It is often paired with acetaminophen or other pain relievers.

Common Opioids	
Oxycodone	**Examples:** OxyContin®, Percocet®, Percodan®, Tylox®
	Methods of use: Usually combined with acetaminophen or aspirin (except for OxyContin)
	Effects: One and a half to two times stronger than morphine
	Street names: "hillbilly heroin," "oxy," "roxy"
Hydromorphone	**Example:** Dilaudid®
	Methods of use: Consumed orally, injected
	Effects: Five times stronger than morphine (oral); eight times stronger than morphine (injectable)
	Street name: "de-la-la"
Oxymorphone	**Example:** Opana®
	Effects: 10 times stronger than morphine
Tramadol	**Examples:** Ultram® and Conzip®
	Effects: 10% the strength of morphine
	Notes:
	• It was originally marketed as non-addictive but is now recognized as having that potential.

Opioid Intoxication Syndrome Signs and Symptoms*	
Constipation	Pinpoint pupils that are unreactive to light
Loss of consciousness	Sedation
Nausea	Slowed breathing

* Monitor the person's respiration and blood oxygen levels, as emergency medical care is often required in overdose situations. Clients may have problems staying awake, so beware of this fall risk. Staff members should be trained in naloxone administration, and naloxone should be readily available.

Opioid Withdrawal Syndrome Signs and Symptoms*		
Anorexia	Goosebumps	Running nose
Anxiety	Hot and cold flashes	Stomach cramps
Cravings	Insomnia	Sweating
Depression	Irritability	Uncontrolled movements
Diarrhea	Itching	Vomiting
Dilated pupils	Muscle pains	Watery eyes
Fever	Nausea	Yawning

* Those showing symptoms should receive supportive care.

Opioid Withdrawal Syndrome Progression
Symptoms appear within 6–8 hours of last dose.
Symptoms peak on the second or third day.
Symptoms usually disappear within 7–10 days, though methadone withdrawal can last several weeks.
Post-acute withdrawal symptoms continue for months.

Cannabinoids

Cannabis is the most used illegal (in many places) drug in the world. It contains more than 565 chemicals, at least 120 of which are cannabinoids. The two main cannabinoids are Delta 9 tetrahydrocannabinol (THC), which is the primary psychoactive ingredient in cannabis and results in a "high," and cannabidiol (CBD), which is not psychoactive and tends to be more relaxing. THC comes from the *Cannabis sativa* plant, whereas CBD comes from the *Cannabis indica* plant. Numerous hybrid plants also exist with varying amounts of CBD and THC.

Common Forms of Cannabis	
Marijuana	**Methods of use:** Smoked, consumed orally **Effects:** When eaten, the effects are stronger and last longer since cannabis is metabolized by the liver into other more potent chemicals **Withdrawal:** Longer process than stimulants or opioids (quitting feels easy at first to people who regularly use)
THC concentrates	**Origin:** Extraction (boiling plant in alcohol) produces a viscous liquid; pressurized butane is sometimes used **Methods of use:** Liquid is dried and smoked; liquid is mixed with marijuana or tobacco and smoked **Street names:** "hash oil," "dab," "amber," "shatter," "shattered glass" **Notes:** • THC content can range from 20%–90%.
Synthetic cannabinoids (cannabimimetics)	**Methods of use:** Dissolved and applied to inert plant material, which is dried, crushed, and smoked; often sold as incense or potpourri at "Head Shops" and convenience stores (now illegal in most localities) **Effects:** Similar to marijuana, but use can cause anxiety, aggression, elevated heart rate, vomiting, psychosis, paranoia, seizures, and excited delirium—all of which are uncommon with marijuana.

Common Forms of Cannabis	
Synthetic cannabinoids (cannabimimetics) (continued)	**Street names:** "spice," "K2," "JWH-018" or 1-pentyl-3-(1-naphthoylindole)—and other JWH series **Notes:** • Cannabimimetics consist of synthetic chemicals that mimic THC but bind more readily to endocannabinoid receptors, creating a stronger response. • They usually do not produce a positive result for THC on drug screens.

Cannabis Intoxication Syndrome Signs and Symptoms		
Bloodshot eyes	Hallucinations in high doses	Paranoia
Decreased anxiety	Hyperemesis*	Problems tracking with eyes
Dilated pupils	Impaired memory, judgment, and learning	Relaxation
Dry mouth		Slowed thinking
Euphoria, laughing, and giddiness	Increased appetite	Time distortion
	Increased heart rate	

* Hyperemesis, or cyclical vomiting syndrome, can cause profuse vomiting, abdominal pain, and other gastrointestinal symptoms. It is characterized by at least weekly cannabis use and onset of cannabis use as an adolescent. Frequent hot baths can offer some relief, with symptoms resolving after cessation of cannabis use (Lua et al., 2019).

Cannabis Withdrawal Syndrome Signs and Symptoms		
Anger	Hyperactivity	Restlessness
Anxiety	Insomnia	Stomach pain
Cravings	Irritability	Sweating
Depression	Loss of appetite	Tremors
Difficulty concentrating	Nausea	

Psychedelics

There are three overlapping classes of psychedelics: entactogens, dissociates, and hallucinogens. Entactogens are drugs that change mood and increase empathy, while dissociates create a feeling that the person using is outside of their body or in a different reality. Hallucinogens present the widest variety of effects of any drug class as they increase insight, intensify or distort perceptions, impair judgment, and create feelings of "oneness" or connectedness.

The effects of all drugs are influenced by a person's environment and mindset, but these variables are greater with psychedelic plants and chemicals. Psychedelics also lack the dependence profile (specifically a defined withdrawal syndrome) of alcohol, opioids, and stimulants. Although psychedelics have been used by civilizations around the world for thousands of years for spiritual and medicinal purposes, many of these civilizations would not condone casual or recreational use of these substances.

Common Entactogens	
Methylenedioxy-methamphetamine (MDMA)	**Origin:** Synthetic, human-made drug that is related to some plant substances (notably sassafras and safrole)
	Effects: Causes a greater release of serotonin than dopamine compared to stimulants
	Methods of use: Consumed orally with other drugs; rarely found in pure form—adulterants are usually present
	Street names: "ecstasy," "Molly," "Adam"
	Notes:
	• It cannot be taken regularly, as it loses its effectiveness if taken on a regular basis.

Entactogen Intoxication Syndrome Signs and Symptoms		
Agitation	Feelings of self-awareness, acceptance	Nausea
Anxiety		Nystagmus
Confusion	Headaches	Pleasure senses heightened
Dehydration	Hyperthermia	
Dilated pupils	Increased energy	Serotonin syndrome**
Excited delirium syndrome*	Increased sex drive	Sweating
	Jaw clenching	

* Excited delirium syndrome involves the sudden onset of agitated or violent behaviors along with hyperthermia. Like other forms of delirium, this is a medical emergency, requiring immediate care.

** Serotonin syndrome is caused by too much serotonin and requires immediate medical assessment and intervention. Symptoms include diarrhea, restlessness, elevated body temperature, tremors, cognitive changes, rigidity, and delirium. The mortality rate is 10%–15% among untreated clients, so intoxicated and withdrawing clients should be monitored.

Common Hallucinogens	
Lysergic acid diethylamide (LSD)	**Methods of use:** Consumed orally, often on blotter-paper or in sugar cubes
	Time to brain: Effects start around 20 minutes, peak at 2–4 hours, and can last 6–12 hours
	Effects: Rather than causing a person to see and hear things that are not there, LSD changes perceptions of things (and people) who are with the person; "bad trips" are often a panic reaction to the drug and are described as nightmarish; tolerance develops very quickly but disappears days after cessation of use
	Street names: "LSD," "acid"
	Notes:
	Lysergic acid diethylamide is the most widely used hallucinogenic and is extremely potent, with doses measured in the microgram (mcg) range.

Common Hallucinogens	
Psilocybin mushrooms	**Origin:** A variety of mushrooms that contain psilocybin and psilocin, naturally occurring psychedelic compounds **Methods of use:** Consumed orally **Effects:** Changes the perception of things that are present (though the effects are generally milder than LSD); lasts for around 6 hours **Street names:** "magic mushrooms," "shrooms"
Mescaline	**Origin:** Found naturally in peyote or San Pedro cacti; can be made synthetically **Effects:** Some visual effects, but most people experience a sense of being completely present and attuned to everything around them; experience lasts 12–15 hours and starts slowly, and it typically involves vomiting before onset of effects **Notes:** • Peyote is used by the Native American Church in ceremonies and should be reserved for members' use.
Dimethyltryptamine (DMT)	**Origin:** Found naturally in numerous plant seeds, vines, tree bark, and other plant materials, or it can be chemically synthesized **Methods of use:** Smoked, sniffed, injected, orally consumed through ayahuasca tea (yagé) **Effects:** Produces vivid, colorful hallucinations—people may feel that they leave their bodies and commune with spirits, aliens, or "others" who guide them; these effects have a rapid onset that lasts 30 minutes or less (known as a "businessman's high") when smoked or injected, while yagé typically causes intense vomiting prior to the hallucinogenic effects and lasts around 12 hours

Hallucinogen Intoxication Signs and Symptoms		
Abnormal laughter	Impaired judgment	Numbness
Anxiety	Increased blood pressure	Paranoia
Difficulty verbalizing	Increased heart rate	Serotonin syndrome
Dilated pupils	Increased temperature	Sleeplessness
Dizziness	Loss of appetite	Sweating
Hallucinations	Nausea	

Common Dissociates	
Dextromethorphan (DXM)	**Origin:** Found in Robitussin®, Coricidin®, and other over-the-counter cough suppressants
	Prescribed for: Suppresses the cough reflex as opposed to acting as an analgesic
	Effects: Little to no psychedelic effects in the doses when used medically; some alteration of consciousness occurs following ingestion of 7–50 times the therapeutic dose over a brief period of time; most people who use DXM report that the "trip," from beginning to end, lasts 5–6 hours with distinctive plateaus; some report an "afterglow" that lasts 24–48 hours after they have come down
	Street names: "dex," "skittles," "triple C's," "robotripping," "sizzurp"
Phencyclidine (PCP)	**Forms:** Liquid, crystal, tablet, powder
	Methods of use: Smoked, snorted, swallowed, injected, often smoked in cigarettes or with marijuana
	Effects: Stimulant, depressant, hallucinogenic, anesthetic, and analgesic properties; low dose lasts for about 2 hours, a moderate dose up to 6 hours, and a heavy dose for much longer; some people develop psychotic reactions that can last for days after the drug is not detectible in their system
	Street names: "angel dust," "fry," "hog," "embalming fluid," "wet"

Common Dissociates	
Ketamine	**Origin:** Derived from PCP, but has only 10% the strength
	Prescribed for: Anesthetic in children and the elderly; a sedative in acute settings; a treatment for severe mood disorders, anxiety disorders, PTSD, and chronic pain
	Methods of use: Snorted or injected and has a quick onset and termination (usually 1–2 hours); when used for treatment purposes, infusion or intranasal administration in low doses
	Effects: Low doses create hallucinations and dissociations—most notably a sense of leaving one's body, journeying out into the universe, and even losing sense of time; people also report detailed near-death experiences (sometimes called "falling down the 'K-hole'"); can cause urinary tract complications when used heavily
	Street names: "special K," "vitamin K," "K"

Dissociates Intoxication Signs and Symptoms		
Agitation, excitement	Excessive salivation	Numbness
Amnesia	Heavy perspiration	Panic attacks
Blank stare	Hypertension	Psychosis
Decreased appetite	Muscle rigidity	Seizures
Dilated pupils	Nausea and vomiting	Slurred speech
Disorientation	Non-communicative	Tachycardia

Inhalants

Inhalants are the only drug class that is defined by its method of use: diverse substances that readily vaporize (Anderson & Loomis, 2003). Although inhalants are sometimes referred to as "volatile solvents," this does not consider substances that people inhale that are *not* solvents. The peak age of inhalant use is 14 to 15 years of age, which then declines by age 19. Inhalant withdrawal begins minutes to hours after the last use and can last hours to days with depression, anxiety, and sleep disturbances continuing for weeks.

Common Inhalants	
Aerosols and solvents	**Used for:** Sprays that contain propellants and solvents **Examples:** Gasoline and fuel additives, airplane model glue, rubber cement, spray paint, paint thinner or stripper, hairspray, deodorants, computer air dusters, correction fluid, writing markers, nail polish remover, coolants (freon), air fresheners **Street names:** "dusting" (canned air dusters), "glading" (air fresheners) **Notes:** • Toluene is the most used solvent and is usually found in other chemicals. • More deaths occur from inhaling gasoline than from any other inhalant.
Volatile nitrates	**Methods of use:** Often used in combination with other inhalants or substances **Effects:** Causes short-term effects of approximately 1 minute; dilates blood vessels so more blood reaches the heart and brain; often used during sexual activity, as the nitrates relax the smooth muscles of the anal sphincter and cause penile engorgement **Street name:** "poppers"

Common Inhalants	
Anesthetics	**Methods of use:** Used in small canisters or from tanks diverted from medical use; commonly used by removing the propellant from canned whipping cream
	Effects: Nitrous oxide replaces oxygen in the blood, so its effects are due to oxygen deprivation; high lasts approximately 5 minutes, but there is a longer impact on people who regularly use anesthetics
	Street name: "whippets" (whipped cream)
	Notes:
	• Nitrous oxide is the most common anesthetic, which acts as a dissociate.

Inhalation Methods (Sharp et al., 1992)
Sniffing: Breathing the substance directly through the nose (insufflation)
Huffing: Inhaling through the mouth or soaking fabric in a liquid solvent and holding it to the mouth
Bagging: Inhaling fumes or a gas from a substance-soaked fabric in a bag (or spraying directly into the bag and putting it over one's head)
Spraying: Dispersing the vapors into the nose or mouth
Balloons: Inhaling the gas from a balloon
Pouring and spraying onto one's clothing to use for sniffing or huffing
Painting fingernails with a volatile solvent to use for sniffing or huffing

Inhalant Intoxication Syndrome Signs and Symptoms		
Cardiac arrhythmias	Loss of inhibition	Sudden sniffing death syndrome*
Coma	Memory impairment	Suffocation
Dilated pupils	Muscle weakness	Tremor
Dizziness	Nausea	Unsteady gait
Euphoria	Respiratory distress	Vomiting
Fatigue	Slurred speech	Wheezing
Hallucinations	Smell of chemicals	
Loss of coordination	Stupor	

* Sudden sniffing death syndrome is the leading cause of death related to inhalant use. It can occur when a person uses inhalants and becomes startled or scared, which can lead to a heart arrhythmia and ultimately cardiac arrest. This can even occur hours after use. It is caused by the action of some solvents, which inhibit the heart's ability to manage an adrenaline surge.

Inhalant Withdrawal Syndrome Signs and Symptoms		
Anxiety	Headache	Restlessness
Depression	Nausea and vomiting	Runny nose
Hand tremors	Sleep disturbance	Visual hallucinations

GAMBLING DISORDER

Although not a physical substance, gambling can be as addictive as some drugs to certain people. Gambling disorder is the only behavioral addiction recognized in the DSM-5. Although gambling disorder is not a SUD, it shares many similarities with the criteria for SUD. For example, people with gambling disorder are often preoccupied with gambling, need to increase the monetary amounts they gamble with more to feel excitement, have trouble cutting down or stopping gambling, continue to "chase their losses" despite continuing to lose money, and lie to hide their gambling. Like SUD, compulsive gambling negatively impacts nearly all aspects of a person's life (APA, 2013).

Ways People Gamble

- Casino games (e.g., slot machines, cards)
- Sports betting
- Stock purchases
- Lottery tickets
- Games of choice (e.g., bingo, internet gambling)

Gambling disorder often begins in adolescence or early adulthood and can co-occur with SUD or "replace" another addiction. For example, a person with alcohol use disorder may become sober and then develop a gambling problem. An ongoing challenge of treating gambling disorder is the client's lack of awareness that it is a problem. The *gambler's fallacy* often comes into play whereby the person mistakenly believes that the probability of winning increases with accumulating losses (e.g., "I've lost four in a row, so I'm due for a win") or only sees small wins despite big losses (e.g., winning a $50 lottery ticket after spending $75 on tickets).

It is important to treat gambling disorder alongside any co-occurring SUDs. Typically, treatment begins by using MI to engage the client, while CBT can then help clients recognize their gambling triggers, learn and practice gambling refusal skills, develop alternative coping strategies, expose biases and distortions related to gambling, and reinforce positive behavioral changes. Gamblers Anonymous, a 12-step group modeled on AA, may also be helpful for some clients.

Assessing Your Substance Use

Understanding your relationship with substances is an important part of the treatment process. Use the following questions to help you examine that relationship and look at ways to make changes.

Substance: _____

How old were you when you first used it? What do you remember about the places and people you were with?

What types or forms have you tried? What are you using now?

What made you decide to try it?

How did you feel when you first started using? What did the high feel like to you?

What are the ways you first used it (e.g., swallow, snort, inject, smoke)?

How do you use it now?

How long have you been using?

How often do you use it? How has this changed since you started using?

How much time do you spend each day using?

How do you get the money to support your use? What are things you regret doing to get money?

How has your use impacted your physical health?

How has your use impacted your mental health?

How have people in your life reacted to your use?

How many times have you tried to stop using? What caused you to start using again?

When you have stopped using, what helped you not use?

When you have stopped using, how did you feel? What symptoms did you experience?

Have you ever overdosed? What happened? Were you treated in a medical facility?

What do you believe keeps you using?

Are you thinking about not using? If you are thinking about stopping, why do you want to stop?

How do you envision your use to be in a year's time?

Assessment of Substance Use Disorders

SCREENING AND ASSESSMENT: ASKING THE RIGHT QUESTIONS

It is extremely important to be as thorough as possible when determining whether a client may have a SUD. There are different ways to evaluate someone for a SUD, but in most cases, some type of screening will occur before an assessment. The terms *screening* and *assessment* are often used interchangeably, but in health care, they describe separate things. A screening, which is brief and narrower in scope, refers to the process of determining whether a client needs further assessment. An assessment refers to the process of conducting a more comprehensive evaluation to further define the problem. Therefore, when evaluating for a potential condition like SUD, a health care professional will screen clients for possible substance use behaviors using standardized screening tools. This can occur in any health care setting. Positive screening results can indicate the need for further assessment or a brief intervention by a professional.

Whether you are conducting a screening or assessment, I cannot understate the need for you to be trained, empathic, and motivated in your work. The very best assessment cannot overcome an untrained, uncaring, or apathetic clinician. Recall that it is important to see clients as more than just their disease. This needs to begin as soon as possible for the client's best chance of recovery, especially here at the screening stage. You should continue to use this opportunity to lessen the stigma and attract people to treatment in every way possible.

Before the screening or assessment even begins, it is important to consider the context and setting of the evaluation:

- How is the room or interview space set up? How comfortable is it (e.g., furniture, room temperature)?

- How safe is the overall environment? (One clinic I worked in had SUD and behavioral health services in the basement. Several clients with trauma histories refused to go downstairs, so we changed where we conducted our interviews.)

- Are there any potential distractions, intrusions, or avoidable interruptions?

- What are other ways to make the client, particularly if they are anxious, traumatized, or confused, feel safe?

It is also important to take time to connect during the initial meeting. People usually want to talk and tell their story, so give them that chance by asking them questions about themselves:

- "Why are you here?"

- "What can we do for you?"

- "How long has this been a problem?"

- "Has anything helped in the past?"

- "Why are you looking for help now?"

Ask simple opening questions and then provide time for the client to talk with as few interruptions as possible. I recommend against typing on a computer while your client talks and instead take minimal notes. *Really listen* to them—you might be surprised by how much you learn!

Screening Tools

There are several different screening tools available when working with clients with SUD. In this chapter, I have included the CAGE-AID and the Screening, Brief Intervention, and Referral to Treatment (SBIRT) as two examples.

The CAGE-AID is a publicly available four-question tool that screens for possible drug and alcohol use. The name comes from an acronym made up of the first letter of each key phrase in the four questions—cut down, annoyed, guilty, and ever (or eye-opener).

The SBIRT is a broader approach to identifying those at risk for SUD and contains three major components. First is the use of a standardized screening tool, like the CAGE-AID, to identify the individual's substance use behaviors. Next is a brief intervention, which involves engaging the client in a short conversation to increase awareness of risky substance use behaviors and to enhance motivation for change. Third is a referral for further assessment for treatment.

There are also additional screening tools for SUD, which include (but are not limited to) the following:

- The Alcohol Use Disorders Identification Test-Concise (AUDIT-C) is a three-question tool that identifies clients who may have alcohol use disorder. It is available in the public domain (Bush et al., 1998).

- The Drug Abuse Screening Test (DAST-10) is a 10-question tool that measures a person's use of substances *other than* alcohol and nicotine (Skinner, 1982).

There are many SUD screening tools, and I prefer the AUDIT-C, DAST-10, or the CAGE-AID because they are brief, easy to use, and have high validity in identifying people who require further assessment for SUD.

The CAGE-AID Questionnaire

1. Have you felt you ought to **cut down** on your drinking or drug use?

    Yes = 1

    No = 0

2. Have people **annoyed you** by criticizing your drinking or drug use?

    Yes = 1

    No = 0

3. Have you felt bad or **guilty** about your drinking or drug use?

    Yes = 1

    No = 0

4. Have you **ever** had a drink or used drugs first thing in the morning to steady your nerves or to get rid of a hangover (**eye-opener**)?

    Yes = 1

    No = 0

Score: _____ /4

A score of 2 or greater is indicative of a positive CAGE-AID, indicating that further assessment is needed.

Script for Administering the Screening, Brief Intervention, and Referral to Treatment (SBIRT)

The sample script here walks you through each component of the SBIRT approach. Please note that the statements on this screening form are merely conversation starters for providers to have with their clients, so it is important that you adapt them to your own style. Clients will be forthright if they believe that they are being taken seriously and not judged.

It is imperative that clinicians understand that part of the screening process is to engage clients and attract them to treatment. Utilizing motivational interviewing skills during screening is a must. Clients may screen positive for SUD but not want to talk about this, usually because they are embarrassed. We want to create an environment where the client knows we want to help them. If a client says "no" once, they may say "yes" during their next encounter. However, people may ask: "What if the client is lying?" This is definitely possible. However, even if you are certain that the client is being less than completely honest, until you have a relationship with them, confrontation will not be helpful and will likely only prevent or delay the client's engagement into treatment.

In the following example, the hypothetical client, who uses cocaine, has completed the CAGE-AID with a score of 3.

Introduce yourself as a health care provider:

"Hi _____, my name is _____ and I am a [*name your role or profession*]. I want to ask you some questions about alcohol and other drugs. This is so I can provide the best care for you. I won't share what we talk about with anyone else unless you give me permission to do so. Is it okay if I ask you some questions?"

Notice how the screener is direct in their approach and asks permission from the client to proceed.

Explain screening results:

"I noticed you answered yes to three of the questions on the screening form. Thank you for being honest. I wanted to talk with you because your responses are like the responses of people who have a problem with alcohol or other drugs. Can we talk?"

This is a brief intervention in that the professional explains the results from the screening form. They again ask the client for permission to proceed. If the client says no, then stop and explain that if they have questions in the future, they are welcome to contact you or the clinic. If given permission, then continue the inquiry.

Increase awareness of risky substance use and make referral:

"For starters, do you believe drug or alcohol use is a problem for you? If so, would you like help in changing your use?"

Again, the client is given a choice whether to proceed or not. If they want help, make the appropriate referral.

"If you don't think your use is a problem, how would you know if your use ever became a problem? In other words, what would have to happen for you to think: 'This might be a problem'?"

This gives the client something to consider. The following is a hypothetical scenario in which the client might ask for more information on cocaine, which he admits to using regularly:

Clinician:	I'm happy to share some more information about cocaine, but can I first ask you why use it?
Client:	You know, I've never had someone ask me that question. It's been something I started doing off and on because it feels good. I think I'm doing more than I used to.
Clinician:	What are the good things it does for you?
Client:	Good things? I guess I never thought about it that way. You're always hearing "Don't use drugs" or "This is your brain on drugs…"
Clinician:	Well, we do things (generally speaking) because we like them or they feel good, right?
Client:	Sure.
Clinician:	Okay, so what are the good things cocaine does for you?
Client:	For starters, coke gives me energy.
Clinician:	What else?
Client:	Focus. I get a lot of stuff done when I use coke.
Clinician:	So, there are things that coke does for you that you like, and I admit that these are some things that attract people to cocaine. Cocaine makes people feel good at first, but what about once it wears off? How do you feel then?
Client:	Like shit.
Clinician:	Can you tell me more?
Client:	Yeah. As much as the high is awesome, the crash just sucks. I mean, I feel drained and anxious.

Clinician: Then what do you do?

Client: Get more coke!

Clinician: Okay, so what happens when you run out of coke, or if you have no money to get more cocaine?

Client: [*Exhales slowly*] That's when it sucks.

Clinician: So that's when things go from bad to worse?

Client: Very bad.

Clinician: I really appreciate how open and honest you have been with me during this discussion. Would you like to talk with someone about stopping your use of cocaine or decreasing how much you use?

Client: Do you have anyone in mind?

Clinician: I have some folks who I think can help. Let me get you that information.

ASSESSMENT OVERVIEW

After the screening process, clients who warrant additional follow-up should receive a comprehensive assessment to further define the nature of the problem and develop appropriate treatment recommendations. The ASAM has developed specific criteria for such an assessment to ensure that clients with SUD have all their needs addressed during treatment. According to its recommendations, all clients should receive a comprehensive medical and behavioral health assessment as part of the treatment process, regardless of the service setting. This involves assessing four primary areas of focus (bolded here) plus an additional three areas once the client is stabilized:

A. **Suicide/Lethality Assessment**

B. **Substance Use Assessment**

C. **Mental Status Exam**

D. **Basic Trauma Assessment**

E. Medical and Mental Health History

F. Family and Social History

G. Medical Screening and Physical Examination (in a medical setting)

In the next section, I'll walk through these different areas of focus and provide assessment tools for each.

ASAM CRITERIA ASSESSMENT DIMENSIONS

The ASAM Criteria Assessment Dimensions are designed to guide the assessment process and ensure that each client receives the most appropriate, individualized treatment. A clear understanding of these treatment assessment dimensions is critical for clinicians. Two key themes drive the Criteria Assessment Dimensions:

1. Quality SUD treatment addresses all the client's needs, not just their SUD.

2. Since SUD should be tailored to the needs of the individual, a thorough assessment is imperative.

Note that there is not an "official" ASAM Criteria Assessment Dimensions form. Rather, the dimensions provide a framework for building your own assessment. I have included assessments that are supported by the Criteria Assessment Dimensions, and you are welcome to adapt them for your use.

ASAM Criteria Assessment Dimensions*

Assessment Dimensions	Assessment and Treatment Planning Focus
Acute intoxication and/or withdrawal potential	Assess for intoxication or withdrawal management. Manage withdrawal in a variety of levels of care and prepare for continued addiction services.
Biomedical conditions and complications	Assess and treat co-occurring physical health conditions or complications. Treatment is provided within the level of care or through coordination of physical health services.
Emotional, behavioral, or cognitive conditions and complications	Assess and treat co-occurring diagnostic or sub-diagnostic mental health conditions or complications. Treatment is provided within the level of care or through coordination of mental health services.
Readiness to change	Assess the stage of readiness to change. If not ready to commit to full recovery, engage in treatment using motivational enhancement strategies. If ready for recovery, consolidate and expand action for change.
Relapse, continued use, or continued problem potential	Assess readiness for relapse prevention services and teach where appropriate. Identify previous periods of sobriety or wellness and what worked to achieve this. If still at early stages of change, focus on raising consciousness of consequences of continued use or continued problems as part of motivational enhancement strategies.
Recovery environment	Assess the need for specific individualized family or significant other housing, financial, vocational, educational, legal, transportation, and childcare services. Identify any supports and assets in any or all these areas.

* Used with permission from *The ASAM Essentials of Addiction Medicine, Third Edition* (Herron & Brennan, 2020).

SUICIDE-LETHALITY ASSESSMENT

SUD is a major risk factor for suicidal or homicidal behaviors. Therefore, assessing for lethal thoughts, plans, and behaviors is essential when conducting a comprehensive SUD assessment.

Suicide-Lethality Assessment*

1. Are you having thoughts of killing or hurting yourself? (Or: On a scale of 1 to 10, with 10 being the highest, how would you rate your desire to kill yourself?) If you're not having any current thoughts of harm, have you had thoughts of killing yourself, hurting yourself, or wishing you were dead in the past two weeks?

2. If you're having current thoughts of hurting yourself or have tried to hurt yourself, do you want to hurt yourself without killing yourself?

3. In what way(s) have you thought about killing or hurting yourself?

4. Do you have access to the things you would need to kill yourself? Do you have access to a gun, knives, or medications? (Ask this question even if the person has thoughts of killing themselves by other methods—like jumping or hanging—to get a picture of their environment and access to other means.)

---

* From *High Risk Clients: Evidence-based Assessment & Clinical Tools to Recognize and Effectively Respond to Mental Health Crises* (Brasler, 2019)

5. Why do you want to kill yourself?

6. How long have you been feeling this way?

7. What has kept you from killing yourself even though you're having these urges?

8. Have you ever tried to kill yourself in the past? If so, what did you do? What happened because of this attempt?

9. Who else knows you have these thoughts or urges?

10. How do you think the people who care about you will feel or react if you kill yourself?

11. Has anyone in your family ever died by suicide?

12. What do you think happens when we die?

13. Have you ever been admitted to a psychiatric hospital? (If yes, for what reason? Did you admit yourself or were you admitted involuntarily? If no, have you ever been assessed for suicide in an emergency room?)

14. Do you currently see a psychiatrist or counselor in the community? Have you seen one in the past?

15. If you have worked with a mental health professional before, did you find it to be helpful? What worked? What did not work?

16. Are you having thoughts of killing or hurting anyone else? (If no, have you had any thoughts of killing or hurting someone else in the past two weeks?)

17. In what way(s) have you thought about killing or hurting someone else?

18. Who is this person and why do you want to kill them?

19. How long have you been feeling this way?

20. What has kept you from hurting this other person even though you feel this way?

21. Do you have a history of hurting people? Hurting animals? What happened because of this? Have you ever been charged with assault or malicious wounding?

If during the assessment, it is evident that the client *clearly* intends to harm themselves or others, law enforcement and/or emergency medical services should be summoned, and the client should be transported to an emergency department or crisis-receiving center for further evaluation. Even if it is not clearly evident (i.e., your gut tells you something is "off"), take the more conservative route and getting further assessment for lethality in an appropriate setting like an emergency department.

Safety Planning

In situations where there is limited information from the client or an inability to construct a reliable safety plan, I am typically very cautious in allowing the patient to remain at their home. In these situations, I send them to the hospital for further assessment. Furthermore, if the client refuses to go to the hospital, I initiate the involuntary commitment process. Note that this process will differ from state to state, so you should be familiar with the laws and processes in your area).

Clients who are experiencing suicidal ideation without a specific plan or intent may not require further assessment for hospitalization. In these situations, a safety plan, which includes another person who will help the client, can be used. Safety plans are *not* "Contracts for Safety," which have limited value (Brasler, 2019). Rather, a safety plan is an opportunity to have a conversation and develop a mutually-agreed upon plan to help the client.

Safety Plan*

People experiencing suicidal ideation need help and support. Having a plan that identifies support and structures is integral to any safety planning. (Note: This is designed for clients who are experiencing suicidal ideation without intent or a firm plan.)

1. What are your warning signs or triggers for suicidal or violent thinking?

2. What are some coping skills you can use when these thoughts occur?

3. Where will you be staying and for how long? Who will be with you?

---

*From *High Risk Clients: Evidence-based Assessment & Clinical Tools to Recognize and Effectively Respond to Mental Health Crises* (Brasler, 2019).

4. Are there weapons or dangerous objects on the property? If so, who will secure these items?

5. Which medications do you take, and who will store the medications and help you take them?

6. How will the next three days be structured? Come up with a plan to do things you enjoy during this time.

7. What outpatient resources are available to you?

8. What is your plan if your symptoms return or worsen?

9. Fill in the information for your local crisis center or hotline:

10. Fill in the information for the suicide prevention hotline:

Substance Use Assessment

I. History of the Presenting Problem/Chief Complaint

1. Describe (in client's words if possible) the reason(s) the client is presenting for services today.

2. What is your drug and/or alcohol use like during a typical week?

3. Record your drug use history by filling out the table on the following pages.

4. In what ways has your drug use caused problems for you?

Substance	Route Administered	Amount Used (Per Day)	Age First Used	Last Used	Withdrawal Symptoms
Nicotine					
Caffeine					
Alcohol					
Cannabis					
Other cannabinoids					
Cocaine					
Methamphetamines					
Other stimulants					
Heroin					
Methadone					

Substance	Route Administered	Amount Used (Per Day)	Age First Used	Last Used	Withdrawal Symptoms
Other opioids					
Benzodiazepines					
Other sedatives					
Hallucinogens					
MDMA					
Other psychedelics					
Inhalants					
Other:					
Other:					
Other:					

5. Have you participated in drug treatment before? What kind(s)? What worked? What did not work?

6. What are some things that trigger your use?

7. How has your drug use impacted you?

8. How has it impacted your family?

9. How has it impacted you at school or work?

10. Have you had periods of recovery (or sobriety)? How long did these last, and how did you accomplish them?

11. Have you ever overdosed on a substance?

12. How would you rate your motivation for treatment at this time?

II. Provisional SUD Diagnosis

Note: You should use DSM-5® criteria to formulate a diagnosis. When noting the diagnosis pertaining to each drug currently used, make sure to specify the current severity: mild, moderate, or severe.

Treatment Decision-Making

1. Does the client require medical attention for an acute illness or injury?

   Yes   No

2. Is the client unable to consent to treatment due to a medical condition or injury?

   Yes   No

3. Does the client require medical attention for a withdrawal syndrome related to alcohol or another central nervous system depressant?

   Yes   No

4. Does the client require acute psychiatric care due to current suicidal and/or homicidal ideation, intent, or attempts?

   Yes   No

5. Does the client require acute psychiatric care due to current psychotic symptoms that indicate that they may not be able to care for themselves?

   Yes   No

6. Is the client unable to consent to treatment due to a mental health condition?

   Yes   No

> **Note:** A *yes* to one or more of questions 1–6 warrants consideration of acute inpatient medical or mental health care.

7. Is the client in need of housing or shelter?

    Yes   No

8. Does the client require housing or shelter *and* have primary custody of minor children?

    Yes   No

9. Is the client pregnant?

    Yes   No

10. Does the client require intensive stabilization for a SUD and a co-occurring mental health disorder?

    Yes   No

> **Note:** A *yes* to one or more of questions 7–10 warrants consideration of residential treatment.
>
> A *no* on questions 1–10 warrants consideration of outpatient treatment or intensive outpatient treatment.

11. If the client responds a no answer to questions 1–10, does the client meet criteria for opioid use disorder?

    Yes   No

> **Note:** A *yes* on question 11 warrants consideration of opioid pharmacotherapy.

Mental Status Exam

Appearance:

- ☐ Neat
- ☐ Tense
- ☐ Rigid
- ☐ Unkempt
- ☐ Poor hygiene
- ☐ Appears stated age

Attitude:

- ☐ Cooperative
- ☐ Uncooperative
- ☐ Hostile
- ☐ Guarded
- ☐ Suspicious
- ☐ Regressed

Behavior:

- ☐ Within normal limits
- ☐ Good eye contact
- ☐ Restless
- ☐ Rigid
- ☐ Combative
- ☐ Tremors
- ☐ Poor impulse control
- ☐ Problems with gait
- ☐ Catatonia/stupor
- ☐ Psychomotor agitation
- ☐ Psychomotor retardation
- ☐ Repetitive movements (stereotypies)

Speech:

- ☐ Normal
- ☐ Soft
- ☐ Slow
- ☐ Loud
- ☐ Hyperverbal
- ☐ Pressured
- ☐ Slurred
- ☐ Echolalia

Mood:

- ☐ Euthymic
- ☐ Depressed
- ☐ Anxious
- ☐ Angry
- ☐ Euphoric
- ☐ Withdrawn
- ☐ Sad
- ☐ Frightened
- ☐ Irritable
- ☐ Expansive
- ☐ Anhedonic

Affect:

- ☐ Full range
- ☐ Constricted
- ☐ Blunted
- ☐ Flat
- ☐ Labile
- ☐ Incongruent with stated mood

Thought Process:

- ☐ Goal-directed
- ☐ Circumstantial
- ☐ Tangential
- ☐ Loose associations
- ☐ Word salad
- ☐ Thought blocking
- ☐ Shows preservation

Thought Content:

Preoccupations:

- ☐ Suicidal ideations
- ☐ Homicidal ideations
- ☐ Phobias

Delusions:

- ☐ Grandiosity
- ☐ Paranoia
- ☐ Somatic delusions
- ☐ Delusions of control
- ☐ Ideas of reference
- ☐ Obsessions

Perceptional disturbance:

- ☐ Illusions (sensory misperceptions)
- ☐ Pseudohallucinations
- ☐ Hallucinations
  - ____ Auditory
  - ____ Visual
  - ____ Tactile
  - ____ Olfactory
  - ____ Gustatory

Level of Alertness:

- ☐ Alert
- ☐ Clouded
- ☐ Drowsy
- ☐ Stuporous

Orientation:

- ☐ Time
- ☐ Place
- ☐ Person
- ☐ Situation

Memory:

☐ No evidence of impairment   ☐ Short-term memory impaired

☐ Immediate memory impaired   ☐ Long-term memory impaired

Attention and Concentration:

☐ Normal   ☐ Distracted   ☐ Poor

Reliability:

☐ Good   ☐ Fair   ☐ Poor

Insight:

☐ Good   ☐ Fair   ☐ Poor

Judgment:

☐ Good   ☐ Fair   ☐ Poor

Notes:

_____

_____

_____

_____

_____

_____

_____

Brief Trauma Screen

Prior to conducting a comprehensive trauma assessment, conduct a brief screening for PTSD to determine whether a more thorough assessment is appropriate. The Primary Care PTSD Screen for DSM-5 (PC-PTSD-5; Prins et al., 2015) is an example of one such screening tool and is provided here.

The PC-PTSD-5

Sometimes things happen to people that are unusually or especially frightening, horrible, or traumatic. For example:

- A serious accident or fire
- Physical or sexual assault or abuse
- An earthquake or flood
- A war
- Seeing someone be killed or seriously injured
- Having a loved one die through homicide or suicide

1. Have you ever experienced this kind of event?

   Yes   No

If no, screen total = 0. Please stop here. If yes, please answer the following questions:

In the past month, have you...

2. Had nightmares about the event(s) or thought about the event(s) when you did not want to?

   Yes   No

3. Tried hard not to think about the event(s) or went out of your way to avoid situations that reminded you of the event(s)?

   Yes   No

4. Been constantly on guard, watchful, or easily startled?

   Yes   No

5. Felt numb or detached from people, activities, or your surroundings?

     Yes   No

6. Felt guilty or unable to stop blaming yourself or others for the event(s) or any problems the event(s) may have caused?

     Yes   No

If the client answers yes to the first question on the PC-PTSD-5, and further answers yes to *any* of the questions in the section after, this suggests the need for additional assessment. One of the most well-validated assessment instruments for PTSD is the Clinician-Administered PTSD Scale for DSM-5 (CAPS-5), which is a 30-item structured interview based on the DSM-5 criteria. You can request a copy of the scale through the National Center for PTSD at https://www.ptsd.va.gov/professional/assessment/ncptsd-instrument-request-form.asp.

Medical, Mental Health, Family, and Social History

Mental Health History

1. Current diagnoses: Previous diagnoses:

2. Previous behavioral health treatment:

    a. Provider:

    b. Type of treatment:

    c. Duration:

    d. Effectiveness:

3. Current/previous medications (name, dose, schedule):

4. Family history of mental illness, including suicides, suicide attempts, and psychiatric hospitalizations. Include dates if possible:

5. Appetite:

☐ Normal   ☐ Increased   ☐ Weight gain

☐ Decreased   ☐ Weight loss

6. Sleep:

☐ Normal   ☐ Hypersomnia   ☐ Insomnia

Medical History

7. Illnesses (and treatments, with dates if possible):

8. Injuries (and treatments, with dates if possible):

9. Allergies:

10. Relevant family medical history:

11. Developmental history (learning disabilities, difficulty meeting milestones, parental use of substances):

Educational History

Vocational History

Abuse/Violence Assessment

12. Who do you live with?

13. What are your relationships like with each person living in your home?

14. Do you feel safe at home?

15. Have you ever been hit, kicked, choked, forced to do something you did not want to do, humiliated, or experienced any other form of abuse?

16. Have the police ever responded to a call at your home and, if so, when was the last time this happened?

17. Who is the one person in your life whom you feel you can count on the most? (It's okay to say you don't know or "no one" if that is the case.)

Strengths and Additional Information

18. What do you like to do to relax?

19. How do you spend your free time?

20. What would you say are your strengths?

21. What are the things you and your friends do together?

22. Tell me a little about your current spouse or partner. How about past partners?

23. Do you have a faith system, church, religion, or any spiritual practice that is important to you?

Medical Screening and Physical Examination

It is important to rule out medical causes for a client's behaviors before focusing solely on mental health or SUD problems. Therefore, if you work in a medical setting (e.g., emergency department or an integrated medical, mental health, and SUD clinic), I recommend referring the client to a medical provider who can conduct a concurrent medical assessment along with the previous assessments. If you do not work in a setting with medical services, I highly recommend that you urge clients to be evaluated by a medical provider (e.g., a primary care doctor) as soon as possible, especially if they have not been seen in a year. A basic medical screening should include the following:

- Vital signs
  - Body temperature
  - Blood oxygen level
  - Heart rate
  - Respirations
  - Blood pressure

- Blood work
  - Complete blood count
  - Metabolic panel
  - Blood alcohol level
  - Therapeutic medication blood levels

- Urine testing
  - Urinalysis
  - Urine drug screen

- Pregnancy Test

- **Electrocardiogram (EKG/ECG)**, if indicated (e.g., client is using stimulants)

- **Medical imaging** (if indicated), such as an x-ray or CT scan

- **Physical exam** by a medical provider

URINE DRUG SCREENS

The initial assessment process can also include a drug screening. Urine drug screens (UDS) are by far the most used screens. They are accurate, can detect a lot of substances, and can provide quick results. There are two main types of UDS: immunoassay tests (also called point-of-care tests) and gas chromatography/mass spectrometry combined (GC/MS) test, which is sometimes called lab testing because most treatment providers lack this sophisticated and expensive in-house testing.

Immunoassay tests are much cheaper and can be conducted by providers with little training. While less expensive, immunoassay tests are more likely to result in false positives (i.e., the client tests positive for a substance they did not use) or false negatives (i.e., the client tests negative for a substance they have used). Immunoassay tests are therefore often used as presumptive (or initial screening), while GC/MS tests are used as confirmatory (or definitive) testing.

Some of the more common substances targeted in immunoassay tests include the following:

Abbreviation	Substance(s) Targeted
AMP	Amphetamines (can also detect most methamphetamines)
BAR	Barbiturates
BZO	Benzodiazepines
COC	Cocaine
META OR METD	Methadone
OPI	Opiates (usually only morphine-based substances, not synthetic opioids)
PCP	Phencyclidine (can also detect ketamine or dextromethorphan in high levels)
THC	Delta-9-tetrahydrocannabinoid (marijuana)

Immunoassay tests work by detecting metabolites of substances, which are chemicals that remain after the body breaks down a substance. Thus, immunoassay tests do not pick up the drugs themselves, but their metabolites. Because of this, immunoassay tests can be "tricked" by innocuous substances to create a false positive. Some of the more common substances that can cause a false positive result include the following:

Amitriptyline	Ephedrine	Quetiapine (Seroquel®)
Antibiotics (numerous types)	Fluoxetine (Prozac®)	Risperidone (Risperdal®)
Bupropion (Wellbutrin®)	Haloperidol (Haldol®)	Sertraline (Zoloft®)
Dextromethorphan	Naloxone (Narcan®)	Trazodone
Diphenhydramine (Benadryl®)	Poppy seeds	Venlafaxine (Effexor®)
Doxepin	Pseudoephedrine	Vicks® VapoInhaler™

In addition to false positive results, there are many substances that people can misuse that are usually not detectable by an immunoassay, including the following:

Buprenorphine	MDMA
Caffeine	Methcathinones
Cathinones	Oxymorphone
DMT	Psilocybin
Fentanyl (unless listed as a specific test)	Synthetic cannabinoids
GHB	Tramadol
Ketamine (may result in a positive PCP result)	U4770 and U4990
Kratom	Z-Hypnotics
LSD	

Since an immunoassay test does not directly detect drugs, those who administer the tests have to accept it does not provide the following:

- The source(s) of the metabolite that caused the positive results

- If the substance was taken therapeutically

- How much of the substance was consumed

- When the substance was used

- If the individual is currently intoxicated

- If the person has a SUD

Despite the limitations of immunoassay testing, I believe it has a place in treatment programs, especially when used in conjunction with GC/MS testing as confirmatory testing. For example, if a client denies they have used a substance after testing positive on an immunoassay test, the sample could be sent to a lab for confirmation. In an opioid treatment program I worked in, we used GC/MS testing to see if the client was taking their buprenorphine (the active opioid in Suboxone). Since clients have been known to take a small piece of their Suboxone and drop it into the sample cup to cause a positive result for buprenorphine, we also tested for the presence of norbuprenorphine, a metabolite produced by the body when it breaks down buprenorphine. A positive result for norbuprenorphine would demonstrate that the client had taken their medication.

GC/MS testing, while more expensive and time consuming, can detect a wider range of substances and can also detect the levels of each substance. You need to decide what the cutoff level for each substance is going to be in terms of whether the sample is positive or negative. For example, most immunoassay tests assign a cutoff level of 50 nanograms per milliliter for THC, which means that any result 51 or more counts as a positive test. Therefore, a level of 40 would be negative while 54 would be positive.

It is also important to note that drug levels can increase and decrease even if a person has not used between tests. This is because drug levels change as a result of how substances are stored and metabolized in the body. Therefore, do not assume if the level during test A was 180 and the level during test B was 170 that the person has not used between tests. The results should be read simply as positive or negative.

Substances are detectable for a limited time in all types of UDS. How long each substance can be detected depends on the specific substance, and there are many other factors that impact detection time. The following table provides approximate drug detection times in urine assays with commonly used cutoff levels (Herron & Brennan, 2020).

Drug	Approximate Duration of Detection
Amphetamine	1–3 days
Methamphetamine	3 days
Barbiturates[*] • Short-acting • Long-acting	 1–4 days Several weeks
Cocaine	3 days
Cannabis • Single joint • Heavy use	 2 days Up to 27 days[**]
Opioids • Heroin, codeine, morphine[***] • Methadone (using a specific assay)	 1–2 days 2–3 days
Phencyclidine (PCP)[****]	7 days

Conducting a UDS

Before you begin incorporating drug testing into any treatment program, you need to make sure to put testing policies and procedures in place that follow the legal and ethical standards for your community. Clients should be made aware of these policies and procedures as part of the informed consent process. There also needs to be a physical space set up to conduct UDS that allows clients to maintain their privacy and dignity. For example, do not have clients provide samples in a restroom in the waiting area of your practice.

---

[*] Although tested using different assays, detection times are similar for benzodiazepines.

[**] Longer detection times have been reported by people using high-level THC cannabis daily.

[***] A UDS will generally not detect buprenorphine, fentanyl, and other synthetic opioids unless it is designed to specifically detect those chemicals.

[****] Regular use of dextromethorphan or ketamine can cause a positive result for PCP.

The following are steps you can take to conduct a UDS with your clients as part of regular testing. We used a similar system at my former practice, but feel free to adapt it to the needs of your practice or clinic.

1. Explain to clients the purpose of the UDS and how it is part of the treatment process. I encourage clients to let me know if they have recently used anything prior to conducting the test. Clients may initially be less than forthcoming, but do not take this personally. Remember that UDS have often been used punitively, and clients may be fearful of the consequences of use. Once you demonstrate that you are not there to "catch" them, but instead want to help, I've found that clients will be more likely to be truthful.

2. Have the client leave their purse, backpack, or coat outside the restroom/sample room.

3. Ask the client to empty their pockets and leave any contents outside the bathroom/sample room. Clients can tamper with their screens by substituting someone else's urine or using synthetic urine, which is available online. There are also products that can be added to urine to create false negatives. Limiting what clients can take with them into the collection area can decrease their ability to alter a sample.

4. Have the client wash their hands. Some homemade methods of tampering with a UDS involve putting a small amount of dishwashing detergent under a fingernail and then dipping that finger into the sample for a few seconds. The enzymes in the detergent can alter the sample to cause a false negative.

5. Give the client a sealed specimen cup.

6. Have them go to the restroom, which should be free of any cleaning items that could be added to a screen.

7. Some providers put blue dye in the toilet to discourage clients dipping the cup into the water, while others have clinic staff flush the toilet—I think both are unnecessary.

This is a good place to pause and talk about observed or unobserved drug screening. Some clinics have a staff person accompany the client to the restroom. This can greatly reduce the chance of a tampered sample, but in order for this to be the most effective, the witness must see the urine leave the client's body. In many legal systems, observed screening is an established practice that creates a chain of custody for the sample; the witness can then swear in court that the sample is from a specific person.

Although we considered doing observed drug screens at my former practice, we worked in a small physical space and had few staff to spare, so conducting observed screens for 20 or more clients at a time was daunting. The only benefit of this practice would involve more accurate samples, but it can also discourage people from coming into our program to begin with because they would likely feel stigmatized. Therefore, in the end, we did not do observed screening. Interestingly, once our program was up and running, about 95 percent of the clients would tell us if (or what) they had used prior to giving a sample.

By not using observed samples, we also avoided having to insert ourselves in the criminal justice process when clients had legal system involvement. While I respect the work done by the criminal justice system, I wanted probation and parole officers to do their jobs (which might include administering UDS), while my teammates and I did our jobs. We were part of a treatment program, not an arm of the criminal justice system. Therefore, when a parole or probation officer would ask me for their client's UDS results, I would explain that we did not follow a strict chain of custody as upheld by state statute, so our results were inadmissible in court.

8. Have the client bring the capped sample cup back to the clinic's medical staff.

9. Have the client wash their hands (because you should always wash your hands after using the restroom).

10. Read the urine temperature indicator on the cup within four minutes of collection, which should read between 90 and 100 degrees Fahrenheit. This is an important way to determine whether the sample is valid. Sample cups without a temperature strip are worthless. Although clients can still sneak in a substitute sample and hold it against their body to maintain body temperature, it does limit many other forms of substitution.

11. If you're using an immunoassay test, wait the required time before checking the results. This is very important, as immunoassay tests have a window in which their results are valid. The test takes time to work, and if read too early, it may give a false negative. Likewise, after a certain time, the test results may give a false positive, so results should be read in the timeframe specified by the manufacturer.

12. Most immunoassay tests have two lines for each substance being tested. One of the lines is a validation line, so if there is no line present, then the sample may not be urine. The other line appears if the sample is negative. No matter how faint the line, any presence of a line denotes a negative result. Remember, sample detection is absolute—the samples are either negative or positive; there is no "kind of positive" or "kind of negative."

13. Depending on the testing system you use, the same sample could be sent to a lab for GC/MS testing. This is something we did if the client disputed the results of the immunoassay screen or if we wanted confirmation of the immunoassay results.

14. The results of the screening should be used to guide treatment, including discussions about treatment direction and efficacy.

One last thing to mention regarding UDS is the value of random screens versus scheduled screens. Generally, randomized screens are going to provide a more accurate assessment of possible drug use because they limit preparation time for potential sample tampering. We utilized random sampling in my program by telling clients to come prepared to give a sample when they came to their appointment, but then only chose random clients from whom to sample. Legal programs often assign a client a number or color, and they are instructed to call or text a telephone number at an assigned time during the day or week to see if their number or color has been selected. If so, this indicates a need for them to come in and provide a sample.

OTHER TYPES OF DRUG SCREENS

Given the invasive and potentially stigmatizing nature of UDS, as well as the number of staff that it requires, alternative methods have been developed to identify drug use. None of these methods are as accurate, reliable, or quick as a UDS, but they are being used in some settings.

Hair Testing

Hair cells can collect trace amounts of substances that can be detected long after a substance is used. Any type of hair can be sampled, including head, body, or pubic hair. This method can be used if the goal is to look for any past drug use—for example, months earlier—and the person being tested is in a highly sensitive (or safety-oriented) job. I personally do not think it is useful for treatment purposes because, remember, you are not trying to "catch" your clients. You simply want to see how they are responding to treatment.

Breath

Most people are familiar with the use of breathalyzers by law enforcement officers to determine whether a person is under the influence of alcohol. These machines work by detecting trace amounts of alcohol that have been metabolized and are being excreted through the breath. It is very important that breathalyzer machines be regularly calibrated or they will not remain accurate. People can attempt to "fool" the machine by not taking a deep breath, but as long as they are properly calibrated, breathalyzers can detect alcohol even with small breath samples.

Like observed UDS, breathalyzer results performed properly can be used as evidence in the legal system and are admissible in court.

Saliva

Just as many substances are detectible in urine, trace amounts can also be detected in saliva. This method is attractive to some treatment providers because it is less stigmatizing than a UDS and can also be administered quicker. The problem with saliva testing is that saliva is more susceptible to environmental conditions and to tampering. It is also harder to detect certain substances—for example, cannabinoids.

Sweat

Substance metabolites can be excreted through sweat just as they are excreted through urine. This method involves placing a transdermal patch on the client, which they wear for a week or more. When I was a part of a juvenile drug treatment court, we used drug patches when clients were away on vacation and there was no way to conduct their UDS. The patch was placed prior to the client's departure and then collected and analyzed when the client returned. One of the initial challenges with using this method was that clients claimed their patches fell off due to excessive sweat or time spent in the sun. In order to test this theory, two teammates wore patches for two weeks. I ran over 100 miles, the judge biked hundreds of miles, and one of our attorneys swam several miles per day. None of our patches came off. After this experiment, none of our clients had their patches come off either.

5

Co-Occurring Disorders

DIAGNOSTIC BASICS

Following the end of a full assessment, an initial or provisional diagnosis is made, which provides a road map for selecting initial interventions and developing a treatment plan. This diagnosis is dynamic, not static, and it is developed through a process of elimination. Whenever possible, gather information from collateral sources in addition to that which is reported by the client, and in cases when you are not certain (or need time to gather additional information), defer to a more conservative diagnosis—for example, you may diagnose a client with unspecified depressive disorder instead of major depressive disorder (Frances, 2013).

In addition, when making a diagnosis, it is important to take the following considerations into account:

- The symptoms *must* cause a significant disturbance in the individual's life over a stated minimal time frame that is specific to the diagnosis (e.g., two weeks, six months, etc.).

- The disturbance *must* impact several of the client's life domains (e.g., family, work, health, etc.) unless otherwise specified.

- The disorder *cannot* be the result of a **medical condition**.

- The disorder *cannot* be the result of a **substance of use or medication**.

In this chapter, I'll explore some of the diagnoses that are commonly comorbid with SUD. I'll also provide strategies to engage and treat clients with each of the co-occurring disorders, as well as tools to help clients manage their symptoms and live healthier, more independent lives.

CO-OCCURRING DISORDERS

Co-occurring disorders (sometimes called *dual diagnosis*) are used to describe a situation where a person has a diagnosis of both a mental disorder *and* a SUD. Over half of people with a serious mental illness also have a serious substance use problem, which can complicate diagnosis and treatment (Inaba & Cohen, 2014). I think this is a low estimate. In my experience, most people with SUD have some form of mental health issue and most people with mental health problems have some form of SUD. People with "just" SUD or a mental disorder are outliers. Because many of the symptoms of mental illnesses and SUD are identical, it can be difficult to determine whether a person's symptoms are the result of their mental illness, the effects of a drug, or a combination of both.

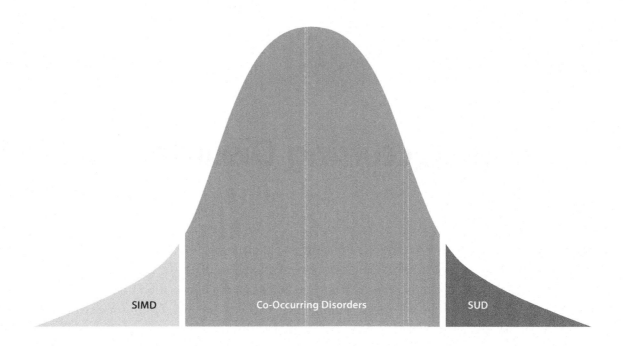

SIMD   Co-Occurring Disorders   SUD

Co-occurring disorders can be divided into two different categories: (1) substance-induced mental disorders (SIMD), which refer to altered mental states that occur as a result of drug use, and (2) nonsubstance-related disorders, in which a SUD exists in addition to a mental illness. It is important that clinicians understand nonsubstance-related mental health illnesses as well as SIMD, as individuals can develop SUD in addition to their existing mental illness. Differentiating the etiology of symptoms takes time, but the following table summarizes some of the main differences between these two categories of disorders.

Substance-Induced Mental Disorders	Nonsubstance-Related Disorders
Client has a history of substance use.	There is no evidence of recent substance use.
Client has no history of mental illness.	Client has a documented history of mental illness.
Symptoms last for a short duration.	Symptoms last for a long duration.
Symptoms can emerge at any time.	Symptoms usually start in late adolescence or early adulthood.
Symptoms vary in severity over several hours.	There is minor variation in symptoms over time.
Symptoms stop when the substance is metabolized and excreted.	Symptoms continue without treatment.

In order to meet criteria for a SIMD, the symptoms must occur within one month of an intoxication or withdrawal episode. Most importantly, the client must not have had mental health symptoms prior to the intoxication or withdrawal episode, and the symptoms must be causing significant problems in their life. When diagnosing a SIMD, it is important to specify the substance that precipitated the episode (e.g., cocaine-induced psychotic episode), as the following table illustrates.

Examples of Substance-Induced Mental Disorders	
Substance	**Mental Disorder**
Alcohol-induced…	…depressive disorder
Cannabis-induced…	… bipolar and related disorders
Hallucinogen-induced…	… anxiety disorder
Inhalant-induced…	…obsessive-compulsive disorder
Opioid-induced…	…psychotic disorder
Sedative, hypnotic, or anxiolytic-induced…	…sleep disorder
Stimulant-induced…	… sexual dysfunction
Other/unknown substance-induced…	…neurocognitive disorder

The majority of clients with SIMD can be effectively treated in dual diagnosis or substance use treatment settings, as opposed to being routed to traditional psychiatric care (Herron & Brennan, 2020), but it is important for the treatment to address both their psychiatric symptoms *and* their substance use symptoms. This is the case even if you are unable to discern the specific origin of the co-occurring mental illness (Substance Abuse and Mental Health Services Administration [SAMHSA], 2020).

The following worksheet is intended to be used after the *Assessing Your Substance Use* worksheet in chapter 3, which explores the substances that the client uses. It can help you determine how your client is currently managing their co-occurring mental illness and SUD, followed by some assessment and treatment considerations when working with comorbid diagnoses.

Managing Your SUD and Mental Illness

Substance use often occurs alongside mental illness, so it is not uncommon for people to be diagnosed with both a SUD *and* a mental disorder, like depression or anxiety. Use the following questions to help you determine how you are managing your co-occurring disorders.

What substances do you use?

What do you feel like before you use? What about after?

What mental health disorders have you been diagnosed with?

Who diagnosed you? Do you agree with these diagnoses? Why or why not?

Describe your mental health symptoms.

When do you experience these symptoms? Are they only present when you are using, or do they also occur at other times?

How does using drugs affect your symptoms?

If you are prescribed medications for your mental illness, what are they?

Have any services helped you with your mental illness? Which ones?

Have any services helped you with your SUD? Which ones?

How do your service providers communicate with one another and with you?

Have you ever experienced a mental health crisis before? What happened?

What are some warning signs that you could be headed for another mental health crisis?

How do you think managing your SUD would help your mental health symptoms?

How do you think managing your mental health symptoms would help your SUD recovery?

Substance Use and Psychotic Disorders

SCHIZOPHRENIA AND OTHER PSYCHOTIC DISORDERS

Psychotic disorders are conditions that cause disruptions in a person's thoughts and perceptions. These disorders are defined by five domains: delusions, hallucinations, disorganized thinking or speech, grossly disorganized behaviors, and negative symptoms. The symptoms within these domains are thought to result from an overabundance of dopamine, and most antipsychotic medications work by targeting this substance in the body.

Schizophrenia is the most commonly diagnosed psychotic disorder and one of the most variable mental health disorders overall. In order to meet criteria for schizophrenia, a client needs to exhibit symptoms from two or more of the five symptom groups (with one of the exhibited symptoms being delusions, hallucinations, or disorganized speech) for a significant portion of time over one month. (Residual symptoms must be present for at least six months.) (APA, 2013; Frances, 2013).

Key Features of Psychotic Disorders

1. Delusions

   - Delusions are fixed false beliefs that involve a misinterpretation of perceptions or experiences.

   - They may involve a variety of themes, with persecutory being the most common.

   - Ideas of reference are also common, in which the person believes that certain gestures, television shows, song lyrics, or environmental cues are specifically aimed toward them.

   - Bizarre delusions are clearly implausible.

2. Hallucinations

   - Hallucinations can occur with any sense, but the most common with organic psychotic disorders are auditory hallucinations.

   - They are usually experienced as voices that are distinctly outside of the person's thoughts.

   - Certain types of auditory hallucinations, especially command hallucinations or voices that make a running commentary on the person's thoughts or actions, are indicative of schizophrenia.

   - Hallucinations are not under voluntary control.

- However, not all strange perceptual experiences are psychotic. Illusions are misconceptions of actual sensory stimuli—these happen all the time and are not necessarily indicative of psychosis.

3. Disorganized Thinking or Speech

- The client may move from one topic to another, reflecting tangential thinking and loose associations.

- Their answers to questions may be partially or completely unrelated to the question.

- The client's speech may not make any sense at all, known as word salad.

4. Grossly Disorganized Behaviors

- These behaviors can manifest in a variety of ways, ranging from childlike actions to unpredictable agitation.

- The client may exhibit difficulty with goal-directed behavior, leading to problems with performing activities of daily living (e.g., maintaining hygiene).

- They may appear disheveled, dress inappropriately for the weather, or act bizarrely.

5. Negative Symptoms

- Affective flattening: The client's face appears flat and unmoving, with poor eye contact and body language.

- Alogia: The client exhibits brief, empty replies with decreased productivity of speech.

- Avolition: The client may sit for long periods of time, showing little interest in work or social activities.

Substances That Can Mimic Psychotic Disorders

Stimulants

Side effects of stimulant use can easily be misdiagnosed as schizophrenia or other psychotic disorders. Remember that psychotic symptoms are thought to occur by overactive dopamine in the brain. Stimulants usually over activate dopamine, which is why effects of their use may be similar to psychotic symptoms. But if the client exhibited psychotic symptoms *before* using stimulants, you can infer that their psychosis is not likely due to stimulants (as opposed to someone who experiences psychosis only in the presence of substance use). However, if a person is experiencing psychosis and is a danger to themselves or others, or they are unable to care for themselves due to their psychosis, they need immediate help—regardless of the cause of their psychosis. Some people with schizophrenia seek out stimulants, but I have found that most people with psychotic disorders avoid stimulants as they exacerbate their symptoms; therefore, they prefer depressants instead.

Cannabis

Cannabis can also cause psychotic symptoms, especially in people who may be predisposed toward psychosis. (It can also cause paranoia in people who do not have this predisposition, but not with the intensity that would be seen in someone with a psychotic disorder.) High levels of THC may exacerbate this. Synthetic cannabinoids are far more likely to cause psychotic symptoms, which can be unnerving to those expecting a typical marijuana high who are suddenly faced with unanticipated symptoms. Although people with schizophrenia may use cannabis to try to moderate their symptoms, cannabis use can interfere with the efficacy of some antipsychotic medications.

Psychedelics

The extent to which psychedelics can mimic psychosis is heavily dependent on a person's mindset and the setting in which they are using. If the person is not in the right headspace or physical space, their experiences on certain psychedelics (especially at higher doses) can mimic psychosis. This is an important—but not the only—reason that people using psychedelics often have people ("sitters") with them when they use. These sitters are familiar with psychedelics but are not using in that moment, and they can reassure the people who have an unpleasant experience while using or summon additional help if necessary. People with schizophrenia rarely seek out psychedelics.

Alcohol

Finally, alcohol can cause psychotic symptoms in the case of Wernicke-Korsakoff syndrome (WKS), which refers to a set of medical conditions that are distinct but often co-occur in people who have used alcohol heavily for years. WKS occurs due to a lack of vitamin B complex (particularly B1), which can happen because of heavy drinking. Korsakoff syndrome leads to dementia symptoms, whereas Wernicke syndrome is a medical emergency that can result in delirium, including psychotic symptoms. About 80 percent of people with Wernicke syndrome also have Korsakoff syndrome (Herron & Brennan, 2020). These conditions require intensive medication intervention. Depressant withdrawal syndrome can also lead to psychotic symptoms in rare occasions. Like the other examples, the psychotic symptoms generally fade over several days to weeks (with the exception being WKS).

Case Example

A complete assessment, including a physical examination and diagnostic testing, can help identify the causes of psychotic symptoms. It is important to rule out any medical emergencies causing the psychotic symptoms that, left untreated, can be fatal to the client. The first assessment that I completed in an emergency department (ED) setting is a good example of why this is necessary.

The client, Brenda, was a 48-year-old female who came to the ED complaining of hearing voices. She was frightened and anxious about her symptoms. I established rapport with her easily, and it was clear to me that she was responding to internal stimuli. Brenda said that the voices had started about six weeks earlier and had been getting progressively louder to the point that they were shouting at her. She would wince when they yelled. Brenda was aware that the voices were hallucinations, but she noted "they are real to me."

Brenda did not have a history of psychosis or any other mental health disorder. Her UDS was negative for any substances we tested. She did not have a history of brain injury, and she lived independently, working in the service sector. Brenda noted that she drank heavily, but not to the point where she believed it caused any problems for her. She had not had a drink in over two days and denied any other alcohol withdrawal symptoms. The medical doctor noted her blood pressure was high, but not critically so.

I called the psychiatrist, who was new to the hospital, to see if he would admit Brenda as a psychiatric admission. He asked what I thought was going on.

"Well, she's too old for this to be a first psychotic break," I said.

"Not impossible," he responded. "But unlikely. What else could it be?"

"I'm thinking alcohol-induced psychosis, either due to withdrawal or her prolonged use," I replied.

"I think you may be onto something," the psychiatrist said, "but ask the ED doc to take a CT scan of her head please."

I explained this request to the ED doctor, who agreed to order the scan. I then went to see another client on the psychiatric unit. After I had finished with that client, I ran into the psychiatrist.

"Hey, that patient you tried to send me? She's bleeding in her brain," he said.

Shocked, I returned to the ED and found the doctor.

"She's bleeding in her brain?" I asked.

"Yeah," the doctor said. "She'll be a medical admission. I just talked with her. I'm working to reduce her blood pressure, which should help. I should have thought to order a CT in the first place, given that she did not have a history of psychotic symptoms—and as you can see, there are other things that can cause psychosis."

"Wow," I said.

"Two things are certain," the doctor continued. "The first is that she does not belong on the psychiatric unit; she needs to be on the medical floor. The second is that this new psychiatrist likely saved this woman's life by figuring out what was wrong."

TREATING CO-OCCURRING SUD AND SCHIZOPHRENIA

Schizophrenia has a high rate of co-occurrence with SUD, as approximately 50 percent of clients with schizophrenia use substances (Herron & Brennan, 2015). Clients with co-occurring SUD and schizophrenia can benefit from integrated treatment approaches that treat both illnesses. Not every client requires inpatient or even intense treatment, but many clients with schizophrenia benefit from case management and care coordination to ensure treatment continuity and service delivery, especially when services are provided by separate agencies. Case management can improve medication adherence—both in terms of antipsychotic medications and medications to treat addiction. Some case management programs are based on Assertive Community Treatment (ACT) models, which have case managers or clinicians visit clients daily to ensure they are safe, have enough to eat, and are taking their medication. Even outside such intensive services, case management can help with housing, food, transportation, and medical concerns. It is important to help the client create a daily routine or structure while also protecting their right to live as independently as possible.

Substance Use and Mood Disorders

MAJOR DEPRESSIVE DISORDER

The most common mental health disorder that co-occurs with SUD is major depressive disorder (Herron & Brennan, 2020). The high degree of comorbidity between these conditions is likely due to clients' use of substances as a means to combat their depressive symptoms. Indeed, clients with SUD often report increased feelings of depression prior to use, cessation (or lessening) of depressive symptoms when using, and a return of depression when they are not using. Thus, depression is a powerful motivator to continue substance use.

The major diagnostic features of depression include low mood or anhedonia combined with at least four other symptoms—such as insomnia (or hypersomnia), difficulty concentrating, decreases (or increases) in appetite, and feelings of worthlessness or guilt—for at least two weeks (APA, 2013; Francis, 2013). Some of the affective symptoms of depression can include increased agitation, irritability, and anger outbursts, as well as excessive worry, anxiety, and brooding. Phobias, somatic complaints, and chronic pain are also common. Although people with mild depression may appear to be functioning normally, doing so causes them to expend a lot of energy. They are also prone to misinterpret normal daily incidents as evidence to support their negative self-concept. Suicide is a possible mortality outcome of depression, occurring in about 10 percent of cases, but even untreated depression that does not result in suicide can lead to higher mortality due to medical illness.

Substances That Can Mimic Depression

Alcohol

Chronic or excessive alcohol use, including alcohol intoxication and withdrawal syndromes, can cause depressive symptoms. Alcohol is, after all, a depressant that generally slows things down throughout the body. Its depressant effects during withdrawal can persist even after a person has stopped using substances.

Stimulants and Cannabis

Stimulant and cannabis withdrawal can also cause feelings of depression, either because the client is adjusting to the absence of the substances that helped give them a "boost" or because they reexperience the depressive symptoms that led them to use in the first place. In all these cases, treating the underlying depression is an important aspect of SUD treatment.

Entactogens and Hallucinogens

The resolution phase of entactogens and hallucinogens can cause depressive symptoms, primarily because these substances cause the brain to release high amounts of serotonin. The brain needs time to replenish its supply of serotonin, and while this is happening, those who use may feel depressed. This depression is typically short-lived unless the client has an underlying depressive disorder, which can require treatment.

BIPOLAR I DISORDER

Bipolar I disorder is characterized by an abnormal, persistently elevated, expansive, or irritable mood, as well as persistently increased activity and energy. This mood will be present nearly every day, lasting for most of the day, for a period of at least one week. During mania, clients often describe their mood as "feeling on top of the world" or "feeling high without drugs." They may also experience mood lability, in which rapid shifts in mood occur (e.g., shifting from happy, sad, angry, and then back to happy again). The increase in goal-directed behaviors (and inflated sense of self-confidence) can lead them to engage in multiple, overlapping projects. They also experience a decreased need for sleep—this is a major indicator of mania—and they will often engage in risky or dangerous behaviors.

In addition, when a client is in a state of mania, their speech is often loud and pressured; another person cannot get a word in edgewise. They may have racing thoughts and the speech itself may make no sense; it can involve singing and be overly dramatic. If the client is irritable, their speech is often hostile, threatening, and abusive, which can lead people close to the client to exclaim, "This is not at all like them. They never say things like that!" Following the end of a manic episode, a client may transition into a hypomanic or depressive episode, or they may return to a sense of normalcy (euthymia). Many people transition from mania to severe depression.

Though bipolar disorder is far less common than major depressive disorder in the general population, people with bipolar disorder are more likely to have a SUD than people with major depression (Herron & Brennan, 2020). The manic and depressive phases of bipolar disorder each play a role in developing a SUD. The depressive episodes are usually more severe than those in major depressive disorder, so clients may more readily turn to substances for relief. On the other hand, manic or hypomanic episodes can cause these clients to engage in risky behaviors, including substance use. When clients with bipolar disorder transition *between* these phases, they may also want to use substances to help relieve the discomfort of going from manic to depressive or vice versa.

Substances That Can Mimic Bipolar Disorder

Stimulants

Stimulants over-excite the brain, so they can cause behaviors that are easily mistaken for a manic episode. Since many people with bipolar disorder also use substances, it can be difficult to determine whether the presenting problem is the result of a substance or not. However, if a client has experienced a manic episode in the absence of drug use, this strongly suggests a diagnosis of bipolar disorder as opposed to a substance-induced manic episode. In either case, people who are actively manic are often unable to care for themselves and may present a danger to themselves due to their extremely impulsive actions. Therefore, many end up requiring hospitalization, which provides an opportunity to determine the cause of the symptoms. If the manic symptoms are substance-related, they will generally abate once the substance is eliminated from the client's body during the hospital stay. Clients with manic symptoms due to underlying bipolar disorder usually respond to mood-stabilizing medications, but this takes time.

Psychedelics and Depressants

Psychedelics, particularly those that also have stimulant-like effects (e.g., MDMA), can also cause symptoms similar to a manic episode, as can depressants. Although depressants (by the nature of their name) tend to reduce arousal, some people can experience paradoxical stimulant reactions to certain depressant medications. For example, one of my brothers becomes hypomanic when he takes diphenhydramine (the active ingredient in Benadryl®), though it makes most people drowsy. At baseline, my brother is nothing close to hypomanic, so this came as quite a surprise to our mother when we were kids and my brother would start bouncing around the room when he got Benadryl due to an allergic reaction. Mom eventually figured this out.

TREATING CO-OCCURRING SUD AND MOOD DISORDERS

When treating co-occurring SUD and mood disorders, the current best practice is to treat the SUD first and then evaluate mood disorder symptoms when the client is no longer intoxicated or in acute withdrawal. That's because if the depression or mania is due to a substance, the symptoms will generally remit once the substance is excreted, which negates the need for antidepressant or mood-stabilizing medications. If the mood symptoms persist beyond acute withdrawal stage, you can evaluate the need for possible pharmacological treatment of the mood disorder.

While medication is generally accepted as an effective form of treatment for mood disorders, controversy remains in some SUD treatment settings where the use of any mood-altering medication is viewed with suspicion or outright hostility. To be clear, these are outdated views and have likely done more harm than good to clients given the high comorbidity of SUD and mood disorders.

Many clients note that they will not "feel clean" or that they will be judged by others in the recovery community for not "really being in recovery" if they take medications. When they bring this up, I listen to them nonjudgmentally and then offer my clinical opinion. I remind them that if they needed treatment for diabetes, asthma, or hypertension, no one in the recovery community would object, and that objections to appropriate treatments for mental illness are another form of stigma toward those with SUD (although this stigma is within the SUD community itself). I also emphasize that their medical history is their business and they do not have to share it with anyone they don't want to.

In addition to medication, psychotherapy has been an effective treatment for depression and bipolar disorders for decades. This can include CBT to help clients understand their negative self-talk, work through their substance- and mood-related triggers, and develop strategies to maintain their health and recovery. Psychodynamic approaches can also help clients understand the unconscious drives that may contribute to their mood disorder or substance use, as well as how family dynamics play a part. Likewise, family therapy can engage family members in the recovery process, while group therapy can provide education, problem-solving, and peer support. Groups can also help clients see that they are not alone in their struggles, and clients can role model effective strategies to one another.

Substance Use and Anxiety Disorders

Anxiety disorders are the most common complaints clients bring to mental health treatment. Clients struggling with anxiety often turn to substances to "medicate" their symptoms. However, when they develop a SUD, they can experience severe anxiety when they stop using, as they will undergo withdrawal symptoms. Although there are many different types of anxiety disorders, in this section I will focus on panic disorder, social anxiety disorder (SAD), and generalized anxiety disorder (GAD) because they are most commonly associated with SUD (Herron & Brenna, 2020).

PANIC DISORDER

Panic attacks involve abrupt and intense episodes of intense anxiety, with the symptoms often described as feeling like a heart attack. In fact, many people who experience panic attacks worry that their symptoms are signs of serious underlying medical problems. These attacks are usually unexpected, with no obvious triggers, and their frequency and severity can vary. When someone develops a pattern of repeated and unexpected panic attacks, they can be diagnosed with panic disorder. People with panic disorder gradually narrow their social circles and limit their physical movements to few (if any) places outside their home in an attempt to avoid experiencing a panic attack. Eventually, these individuals can meet the diagnostic criteria for agoraphobia (APA, 2013; Frances, 2013).

SOCIAL ANXIETY DISORDER

SAD, also known as social phobia, is one of the most common forms of anxiety. Situations that can trigger social anxiety include public speaking, meeting new people, or attending social events (like a party), but it can also be events that others may find commonplace, such as making small talk, using public restrooms, or answering a phone call. For individuals with social anxiety, the fear of being judged or humiliated in the context of the social interaction is all-consuming. It can be difficult to determine when shyness, which is not a mental disorder, becomes so overwhelming that it develops into SAD. Unsurprisingly, social anxiety and SUD often co-occur. For example, a person who is anxious about going to a work-related gathering may drink alcohol to feel less anxious (and maybe more confident) about the event. Over time, they may need to drink more to achieve the same feeling, and they find that in the absence of alcohol, they feel more anxious. You can see how this insidious process can lead to SUD.

GENERALIZED ANXIETY DISORDER

People with GAD worry nearly all the time about every aspect of their lives, including their work, family, finances, and health. It is more than just being a "worrywart." People with GAD experience all-encompassing and debilitating anxiety that prevents them from functioning. As you can imagine, using substances—particularly those that slow everything down, like alcohol, benzodiazepines, and opioids—can be very attractive to people with this type of anxiety. Like people with social phobia, individuals with GAD can develop SUD through this process.

Substances That Can Mimic Anxiety Disorders

Stimulants

Stimulant use can mimic anxiety symptoms, particularly the use of more potent stimulants like cocaine and methamphetamine, though excessive caffeine should also be considered when dealing with clients with anxiety symptoms. Use of these substances worsens the impact of preexisting anxiety disorders. Anxiety symptoms are also common complaints among clients experiencing stimulant, opioid, alcohol (and other central nervous system depressants), and cannabis withdrawal. Addressing these anxiety symptoms is an important part of withdrawal management.

TREATING CO-OCCURRING SUD AND ANXIETY

Just as with psychotic and mood disorders, differentiating between substance-induced anxiety and nonsubstance-induced anxiety is difficult, but it can be done by conducting a thorough history and observation of the client when they are not under the influence of substances (Herron & Brennan 2020). Most anxiety symptoms associated with SUD are going to occur when the client stops using the substances they have grown used to. Some of this anxiety is psychological—for example, the client likes how they feel when using the substance and doesn't like how they feel when they are not using. Anxiety can also be physiological when the body's response to withdrawal creates anxiety to motivate the client to use again.

This is made more difficult when you consider that many clients have been placed on benzodiazepines by medical providers or have been obtaining the medications illicitly. Most benzodiazepines, particularly shorter-acting ones like alprazolam and lorazepam, were never intended to be used for an extended time, but they are often prescribed indefinitely, sometimes resulting in benzodiazepine use disorder. The withdrawal management process is often very slow for clients tapering their doses of benzodiazepines—tapering can take months when clients have been using high doses. Medical monitoring is necessary to avoid a withdrawal syndrome similar to alcohol withdrawal (e.g., the danger of delirium tremens and seizures).

Aside from potential medical issues, clients also must deal with rebound anxiety as their benzodiazepine dosage is decreased. This anxiety can be debilitating and may push them to look to other substances as substitutes that can provide relief from their symptoms. Similarly, clients with opioid use disorder experience incredible levels of anxiety as they begin to navigate recovery, so helping them manage this anxiety is a key component of treatment.

Utilizing an MI approach can be helpful, particularly with clients who are ambivalent about making changes. I also recommend mindfulness exercises, yoga, experiential therapies, and regular exercise as ways to help address anxiety disorders, with or without comorbid SUD. CBT can also be helpful for clients to learn how their thinking impacts their behaviors.

Until recently, I was a big fan of group therapy for all clients in treatment for SUD. I have seen group work be extremely effective for a variety of clients, and I believe that most clients can benefit from it. However, group settings may overwhelm clients with anxiety, as well as those who are dealing with trauma, and I think treatment groups need to be sensitive of this and provide alternative forms of therapy should the client ask.

A final word: Anxiety can be contagious. I discovered this when I started working in crisis settings. I thought my experience up to that point had prepared me for working in intense, high-pressure situations, and for the most part I enjoyed the work. The exceptions were the clients who were dealing with panic attacks. Confronted with clients in states of abject terror, I found my heartbeat increasing and felt a lot of anxiety in myself. I then remembered something I had learned in graduate school…breathe! I focused on my breathing, slowed down my speech, and lowered my volume. Just doing this helped me be attentive to what my client needed, and just as I could react to their anxiety, they could react to my calmness. I also reminded myself that this situation was not going to last forever, and that self-talk was often helpful for me.

Substance Use and Posttraumatic Stress Disorder

TRAUMATIC EXPERIENCES

As you learned in chapter 2, the connection between trauma and SUD is substantial, as many people who experience trauma use substances to manage their trauma symptoms. We need to acknowledge that not everyone who experiences trauma will have lasting symptoms, and that not everyone with lasting symptoms will develop SUD, but the majority of people with SUD have experienced trauma *and* struggle with persistent symptoms related to that trauma.

Posttraumatic Stress Disorder

One of the challenges in diagnosing trauma is that many people believe lasting trauma can only be diagnosed as PTSD, which is one of the most complex diagnoses in the DSM-5. PTSD contains a myriad of criterion that can be summarized as:

1. Intrusive, persistent reexperiencing of the trauma: This can include intrusive thoughts (sometimes called flashbacks), distressing memories that are hard to ignore, and vivid, recurring nightmares.

2. Persistent avoidance of people, places, or things that remind the person of the trauma: The avoidance is linked to the knowledge that these things are likely triggers of memories, feelings, and even physiological reactions to the trauma.

3. Negative alterations in cognitions and mood: Severe depression and anxiety are common, as is memory loss (particularly regarding details surrounding the event), self-blame, guilt, hopelessness, social withdrawal, and an inability to experience positive emotions.

4. Marked alterations in arousal and reactivity, sometimes called hypervigilance: This can lead to problems with appetite and sleep or cause the client to feel like they are always on edge. Loved ones may describe the client as easily startled, irritable, angry, or unable to concentrate (SAMHSA, 2020).

I have found that clients with SUD may not meet all these criteria, but if they have experienced some form of trauma, they may have some symptoms of PTSD, and these symptoms can be linked to their SUD. Similar to people with anxiety disorders, clients with trauma may seek out substances to help them sleep, take the edge off, forget their traumatic experiences, or decrease their overall anxiety. This can lead to a state where the person only feels "normal" when using. Thus, the idea of stopping use, even when faced with overwhelming negative consequences (e.g., loss of job, family, housing) is untenable.

Substances that Can Mimic PTSD

Unlike mood or psychotic disorders, substances do not mimic the symptoms of PTSD. The exception would be substances that can mimic anxiety disorders, which can imitate some of the anxiety symptoms of trauma-related disorders. The main issue with co-occurring SUD and trauma-related disorders is recognizing the presence of both disorders and appropriately treating them.

Case Example

I was recently part of a discussion with two certified peer recovery specialists, one of whom, Brian, worked in a harm reduction clinic.

"I've been in recovery for 17 years," Brian said. "And for the first 12 years, I was taught that all I needed to focus on were my symptoms. The 12 steps and 12 traditions (of AA) saved my ass at first, but I wondered how I'd gotten there in the first place."

"By 'there,' you mean how and why you developed SUD?" I asked.

"Yeah, I was told I had a disease and that was it. But I was like, 'Why do I have this? Am I just unlucky?' So I started working with a therapist who helped me see that the SUD served a purpose. I had a shit ton of trauma as a kid and an adult and soon found out that my trauma was the main source of my addiction."

"That is something I've seen so often in my clients," I noted. "A lot of trauma is often there."

"I think it's in everyone with addiction," Brian said.

"Trauma?"

"Yeah, and usually more than one thing happens to them. And I think we need to treat the trauma *while* we treat the SUD. This is what I say to the people I work with: 'Treat the cause (the trauma), not just the symptoms (the SUD).'"

When you consider that this statement comes from someone with lived experience, the last sentence is so true, yet many of our practices have yet to align with this perspective.

TREATING CO-OCCURRING SUD AND TRAUMA

Aside from a brief PTSD screening, I do not conduct an in-depth trauma assessment when a client first presents for treatment. One reason for this is that many clients are under the influence of substances when they present, so their ability to recall past events and describe their symptoms may not be accurate. An even more important reason is that delving into trauma can be traumatic in itself and must be done carefully in the context of a caring, empathetic therapeutic relationship, something that is just beginning to form during the assessment. Working with the client over a period of time will produce mutual trust and establish some form of comfort, and then the client will hopefully be in a better state to discuss their trauma (Herron & Brennan, 2015).

As a reminder, processing trauma in groups is not recommended, as these settings can be extremely overwhelming. More importantly, one member's processing can trigger trauma reactions in other group members. I have seen psychoeducational groups provide education about trauma and the different reactions to trauma while also demonstrating coping skills for handling these reactions, but the actual processing of trauma is best accomplished in individual therapy.

Similar to treatment of anxiety disorders, medical approaches should address potential misuse of medications, particularly benzodiazepines. Since many clients with trauma-related disorders initially present to medical providers as anxious, it is understandable that these clients are often treated with antianxiety medications, particularly benzodiazepines. As noted in the previous handout, it is important to take care when tapering down these medications to avoid markedly increasing the client's anxiety. For clients taking medication for treatment of opioid use disorder, the use of benzodiazepines with buprenorphine or methadone is a serious safety concern, as the combinations of these medications can be harmful to clients. Therefore, medication treatment of trauma-related disorders, especially when co-occurring with SUD, needs to be carefully monitored.

Because traumatic memories are often a trigger for the client to use, it can be difficult to establish a sense of safety when clinicians ask clients to delve into their trauma narrative. One alternative treatment option is Seeking Safety, which is an evidence-based, present-focused therapy that asks clients to focus on how they envision safety within their present-day lives, as opposed to focusing on the past. It is a form of manualized treatment that teaches clients various coping skills across the course of 25 sessions—such as setting boundaries, creating meaning, and detaching from emotional pain—so they can gain more control over their lives. I like Seeking Safety because I have seen it help many clients understand that (1) they have experienced trauma; (2) their reactions to trauma, including SUD, do not make them "crazy;" and (3) they have resilience and recovery is possible.

Substance Use and Eating Disorders

ANOREXIA NERVOSA AND BULIMIA NERVOSA

Eating disorders, particularly anorexia nervosa and bulimia nervosa, are some of the most serious mental health disorders. They have the highest mortality rate of any other mental disorder due to the life-threatening effects caused by weight loss and starvation (e.g., emaciation, arrhythmias, hypotension, dehydration, loss of bone mass, growth retardation). They also pose an elevated suicide risk. Therefore, when it comes to eating disorders and substance use, it should come as no surprise that clients with anorexia or bulimia who concurrently use substances have poorer treatment outcomes (Gregorowski et al., 2013).

While there are no substances that mimic the symptoms of eating disorders, eating disorders share many characteristics of SUD, notably compulsions, continued use (or disordered eating behavior) despite its negative consequences, and attempts to hide one's behaviors—so there is understandably high comorbidity between the two. Trauma also plays a substantial role in the lives of people with eating disorders, so clients may be drawn to substances like alcohol, opioids, or other central nervous system depressants that help them feel numb. These substances may also curb their appetite as well. Similarly, clients may seek out stimulants to decrease their appetite and increase their energy, thereby replacing the energy they lose from a decrease in caloric intake. Some common stimulants used by clients with eating disorders include caffeine, ephedrine, methylphenidate, amphetamine, cocaine, or methamphetamine.

TREATING CO-OCCURRING SUD AND EATING DISORDERS

Concurrent treatment is highly recommended for co-occurring SUD and eating disorders, but given the lack of dual-focused programs, the client's substance use may need to be addressed first (SAMHSA, 2020). However, when clients are so dangerously malnourished due to the effects of severe anorexia that hospitalization is needed, it is necessary to first stabilize and treat any underlying medical issues related to their eating disorder. This may include rehydration and refeeding. Given the high death rates associated with eating disorders, clinicians should not treat clients with these disorders unless they have received professional training in this area *and* they are working as part of an interdisciplinary team that includes a medical provider and registered dietitian.

Eating disorder treatment often occurs in partial hospitalization or residential treatment programs, where both group and individual therapy are used. Since eating disorders usually have their roots in family dynamics or family-related trauma, residential and partial hospitalization programs often include a family component as well. Regardless of the treatment setting, family therapy is contraindicated if the family system is extremely unhealthy (e.g., if the family is judgmental or blaming and not invested in helping the client). Individual therapy, often from a trauma-informed approach, can also be used in outpatient settings from a CBT or dialectical behavioral therapy (DBT) approach. Finally, group therapy can be helpful in treating eating disorders, but it is generally best for the client to process the trauma that may have led to the disorder itself in one-on-one therapy.

Substance Use and Personality Disorders

PERSONALITY DISORDERS

Personality disorders are characterized by enduring and maladaptive patterns of thinking, feeling, and behaving that date back to late adolescence or early adulthood. These patterns of relating to the world cause an individual to experience disruptions in their relationships, sense of self, and overall emotional and cognitive functioning (APA, 2013). Currently, the personality disorders are separated into three different clusters: cluster A (odd or eccentric), cluster B (dramatic, emotional, or erratic), and cluster C (anxious or fearful). The following table includes 10 different personality disorders divided by cluster.

Cluster A: Odd or Eccentric (Psychotic)	Cluster B: Dramatic, Emotional or Erratic (Mood)	Cluster C: Anxious or Fearful (Anxiety)
• Paranoid personality disorder • Schizoid personality disorder • Schizotypal personality disorder	• Antisocial personality disorder • Borderline personality disorder • Histrionic personality disorder • Narcissistic personality disorder	• Avoidant personality disorder • Dependent personality disorder • Obsessive-compulsive personality disorder

There is high comorbidity between the cluster B personality disorders, and low comorbidity among the cluster A and cluster C disorders. While the cluster A disorders are often viewed as milder forms of psychotic disorders like schizophrenia, people with these personality disorders are more likely to live independently compared to those with psychosis. In addition, the cluster C personality disorders share many traits with anxiety disorders.

When it comes to SUD, people with cluster A and cluster C disorders have relatively low rates of comorbidity. However, individuals in these two clusters tend to isolate themselves, and it is not known how much this factor (or other things) contributes to the lack of co-occurring substance use. The cluster B disorders have the greatest comorbidity with SUD, with high rates of substance use found in men with antisocial personality disorder (ASPD) and women with borderline personality disorder (BPD). Much of this may be due to inherently unstable moods associated with these personality disorders, as clients with these disorders may seek out substances to regulate their moods.

Similarly, people with BPD often seek out activities and situations that excite them, which can include substances. Like many clinicians, I see BPD as a reaction to trauma, so many of the connections between trauma-related disorders and SUD can apply to SUD and BPD as well. Similarly, the inherent distrust of others and willingness to engage in criminal activities may point to a connection between ASPD and SUD. When you consider the high level of trauma in the lives of most people with ASPD, you can also apply the connections between SUD and trauma when it comes to ASPD.

TREATING CO-OCCURRING SUD AND PERSONALITY DISORDERS

When working with clients diagnosed with personality disorders, particularly the cluster B disorders, it is important to set boundaries at the beginning of treatment. This includes limiting all outside-of-session contact unless you are using a prescribed treatment modality like DBT, which includes coaching calls as part of treatment. Clients with personality disorders are usually in a state of perpetual crisis or near crisis, which can be overwhelming to you as a clinician, so be mindful of transference and countertransference issues and seek supervision as needed.

In addition, it is likely that the client's focus on their treatment will be all over the place, so it is important for them to set goals and objectives and stick with them. I recommend using a CBT-based treatment to help clients understand the interactions between their emotions, actions, and SUD. Peer-led recovery groups can be beneficial because peers who are further along in their recovery can role model healthier behaviors and assist newer members.

Substance Use and Attention-Deficit/Hyperactivity Disorder

ATTENTION-DEFICIT/HYPERACTIVITY DISORDER

ADHD is characterized by persistent problems maintaining attention, giving attention to details, and following through on tasks. Individuals with ADHD tend to be disorganized, forgetful, and easily distracted, and these symptoms persist in a variety of ways. ADHD impacts about 6 percent of the population, with greater proportions among children and adolescents (Saddock et al., 2015). In some areas of the country, ADHD is over-diagnosed, and the symptoms can be better attributed to a learning disorder, trauma, or a mood disorder. However, legitimate ADHD impacts all areas of a person's life, not just their academic or work functioning. For example, problems with following through on tasks can interfere with their ability to maintain friendships, and their difficulties with attention and focus can make it harder to read important social cues. In addition, people with ADHD are often more prone to take risks, which can include trying substances at a younger age. Many clients with ADHD may find that using stimulants (prescription medications and cocaine or methamphetamine) helps them to focus, which can reinforce a desire to continue use.

Psychostimulants like Ritalin and Adderall have long been considered a "front line" of ADHD treatment, as these medications increase focus and attention. There has long been concern about the use of these stimulant medications in young people and its possible link to SUD in later life, but there does not appear to be a connection between the two (Saddock et al., 2015). In fact, for people who truly have ADHD, these medications can make considerable differences in their lives. However, stimulant medication does have a high potential for diversion to people who do not have ADHD and who may misuse these medications by crushing and snorting them to achieve a stimulant high.

TREATING CO-OCCURRING SUD AND ADHD

Providers should be careful when prescribing stimulant medications to clients with ADHD and SUD because of their potential for misuse. This does not mean that stimulants cannot be prescribed for people with both disorders; a client's treatment should be individualized. However, the use of non-stimulant medications to treat ADHD, such as atomoxetine, guanfacine, and clonidine, can limit the possibility that treating the client's ADHD will negatively impact their SUD recovery.

In terms of psychotherapy, group therapy can be helpful, but people with ADHD may find it challenging to sit through groups, so it may be necessary to shorten or segment the group time or incorporate activities into treatment. I have found that group work centered on problem-solving or experiential group activities can be helpful. Individual therapy, such as CBT, can be helpful in addressing the negative thought processes that often accompany ADHD. People with ADHD have often spent a considerable amount of time hearing about their faults and flaws from a young age, usually from loved ones or "in jest," which often leads to low self-esteem and therefore negative self-talk—these thought processes have the ability to trigger substance use.

In either group or individual therapy, clinicians may employ a lot of coaching because clients with ADHD (with or without SUD) often need help in creating structure in their lives or finding a balance with their responsibilities. A psychiatrist I once worked with put it best regarding adults with ADHD: "These are exceptionally smart people. The biggest challenge they face is building relationships with people who understand them and finding work that stimulates them."

6

Treatment Planning—Determining the Correct Level of Care

STAGES OF TREATMENT

Despite society's increasing awareness of SUD, treatment options remain limited for many. Simply put, there is not enough treatment available for people who need it. Less than 25 percent of people with addictive disorders will receive professional treatment in their lifetime, with this number being even lower for cigarette smokers (Herron & Brennan, 2020). It is crucial to ensure the availability of appropriate treatment, making sure that it is tailored to address all aspects of the individual (culture, language, sexual orientation, gender identity, etc.), as well as to the specific drug or substance.

Treatment can be conceptualized as a process that involves four different stages:

- Engagement

- Stabilization/persuasion

- Active treatment

- Continuing care

These stages are seen as a continuum, and clients may move forward or backward multiple times on their journey to recovery depending on a host of factors—but this back-and-forth pattern should not be viewed as treatment failure. People with SUD may even disengage from treatment completely from time to time, but the knowledge they gain during the treatment phases is still seen as cumulative and helps them toward their ultimate goal.

During the first stage, **engagement**, the goal is simply to enhance the client's motivation to work toward change. As you will learn in chapter 7, engaging clients in treatment requires a balance of respecting their right to self-determination with the danger of continued substance use.

After the engagement phase comes **stabilization/persuasion**, in which clients work toward specific goals and make process in recovery (however they define it). This can include managing their withdrawal from substances or treating co-occurring mental or medical issues. Clients who do not elect to stop using may scale back their use or begin engaging in safer practices (e.g., making sure they use clean needles).

Once clients are stable, **active treatment** begins, in which any remaining problematic use is stopped or greatly curtailed, other areas of the client's life are stabilized, and possible reasons for SUD are addressed. Finally, there is **continuing care**, in which treatment programs help clients to continually engage in recovery-oriented thinking and actions. This can involve helping clients with other self-actualization needs they may have (e.g., finding purpose in their lives) while also limiting the potential for a return to use. Please note that clients can return to use at any stage of treatment. This does not mean that treatment has failed, since clients can also return to treatment.

The Stages of Treatment

Engagement:
Clinician enhances
the client's motivation to
work toward change.

**Stabilization/
Persuasion:**
Client works toward
specific goals and makes
progress in recovery.

Active Treatment:
Problematic use is stopped
or greatly curtailed, client's
life stabilizes, and possible
reasons for SUD are
addressed.

Continuing Care:
Treatment programs help
clients to continually
engage in recovery-oriented
thinking and actions.

In this chapter, I'll present various levels of treatment as outlined by ASAM and discuss how to determine which clients are appropriate for each level of care. Before looking at the various levels of treatment, it is important to understand the role of prevention.

PREVENTION

Prevention seeks to deter people from using drugs in the first place. In the case of clients who are using substances or who currently have a SUD, prevention aims to limit the harm related to use. The following are the three types of prevention:

Primary Prevention (Education)	Secondary Prevention (Treatment)	Tertiary Prevention (Harm Reduction)
• Seeks to prevent future drug use • Provides education and refusal skills • Teaches coping skills and strategies to handle peer pressure	• Seeks to stop drug use after it has started • Includes the addition of intervention strategies • Can involve diversion programs, like drug treatment courts	• Does not view abstinence as the only measure of success • Attempts to minimize the harmful effects of substance use

Good prevention efforts consider the fact that simply providing drug information to a person using substances does not usually change their behaviors, and scare tactics are ineffective in preventing SUD. Many prevention programs target the family and the community for a more holistic approach than previous efforts. In addition, while most prevention efforts are geared toward children and adolescents, prevention itself can be a life-long intervention.

Harm Reduction

When prevention efforts involve harm reduction, the goal is to meet the client where they are and reduce any substance-related harm. Harm reduction efforts include limiting the transmission of sexually transmitted diseases (e.g., through condom distribution, needle exchange programs, supervised injection sites), reducing the number of people dying from drug use (e.g., by distributing naloxone and providing fentanyl test strips), providing medication-assisted therapy, and treating comorbid mental illness that can exacerbate SUD. It is important to know where and when harm reduction resources are available in your environment in order to help clients access them.

Please note that while harm reduction is technically not SUD treatment, it does not diminish its importance. Harm reduction strategies can be used simultaneously with treatment. Remember the overall goal is to help clients improve their lives, and for many people, this can start with helping them to reduce mortality or other harms.

Harm Reduction Strategies

Not everyone is ready to stop using substances when they come to treatment. Harm reduction recognizes this fact, and instead of pushing you into abstinence, it encourages you to limit the harm associated with substance use (i.e., injury, illness, or death). Use the following prompts to help you and your counselor discuss strategies to best serve you.

Places you can enroll in medication-assisted treatment:

Places you can obtain clean needles and/or works (paraphernalia):

Places you can get fentanyl test strips:

Places you can get Narcan:

Places you can get condoms:

Places you can get medical care:

Places you can get psychiatric care:

LEVELS OF TREATMENT

Matching clients to the appropriate level of treatment is a process that should occur during the assessment process. Recall that ASAM has highlighted six assessment dimensions based on each individual client to define the severity of the situation and to provide a suitable treatment plan. These include the potential for acute intoxication/ withdrawal (dimension 1), physical health conditions or complications (dimension 2), mental health conditions or complications (dimension 3), and other factors of the client's life, which are assigned a risk rating. The entire list of assessment dimensions can be reviewed in chapter 4.

You should also remember that treatment will be different for each person when taking into consideration the population they fit into, which could be their gender, sexual orientation, whether they have a disability, or other factors. For example, clients with minor children in their care will have different needs than clients without dependents in their lives. A more thorough discussion of specified treatment strategies for special populations is included in chapter 11.

In addition to tailoring treatment to meet the client's needs, the placement of a client should always aim to be the least-restrictive treatment setting possible. The following handout provides a description of the specific levels of SUD treatment as outlined by ASAM.

ASAM Levels of Treatment[*]

ASAM Criteria Levels of Care	Level	Description
Early intervention	0.5	Assessment and education for at-risk individuals who do not meet diagnostic criteria for a substance-related disorder
Outpatient services	1	Less than 9 hours of service per week (adults); less than 6 hours per week (adolescents)
		Comprises individual, family, and/or group therapy using a variety of therapeutic approaches
Intensive outpatient program (IOP)[**]	2.1	9 hours of service or more per week (adults); 6 hours or more per week (adolescents) in a structured program to treat multidimensional instability
		Usually three days per week, for 8 to 12 weeks, and most of the time is spent in group therapy
		Groups are structured with a mix of education, therapy, mindfulness exercises, and experiential learning
		Family members can be involved in weekly group sessions
		Members may be encouraged to attend 12-step groups outside of the IOP
		Like partial hospitalization, can be used as a step-down from (or step-up to) a more (or less) intense level of treatment or as a replacement for residential treatment

[*] Adapted with permission from *The ASAM Essentials of Addiction Medicine, Third Edition* (Herron & Brennan, 2020).

[**] The length of stay included for IOPs and partial hospitalization settings in this table are indicative of an average stay and should not be construed as definitive.

ASAM Criteria Levels of Care	Level	Description
Partial hospitalization	2.5	20 hours of service or more per week, for 4 to 6 weeks, in a structured program for multidimensional instability not requiring 24-hour care Contains much of the content of a residential program (i.e., time is spent in heavily structured groups), but the client lives outside the program Is often used as a step-down from residential treatment or for people with significant co-occurring disorders Can also be used as a step-up from IOP or as a substitute for residential treatment
Residential treatment		
Clinically managed low-intensity residential	3.1	24-hour structure with available trained personnel with emphasis on reentry to the community; at least 5 hours of clinical service per week
Clinically managed population-specific high-intensity residential	3.3	24-hour care with trained counselors to stabilize multidimensional imminent danger; less intense milieu and group treatment for those with cognitive or other impairments unable to use a full active milieu or therapeutic community
Clinically managed high-intensity residential	3.5	24-hour care with trained counselors to stabilize multidimensional imminent danger and prepare for outpatient treatment; able to tolerate and use a full active milieu or therapeutic community
Medically monitored intensive inpatient	3.7	24-hour nursing care with physician availability for significant problems in dimensions 1, 2, or 3; 16 hours per day for counselor availability

ASAM Criteria Levels of Care	Level	Description
Residential treatment (continued)		
Medically managed intensive inpatient	4.0	24-hour nursing care and daily physician care for severe, unstable problems in dimensions 1, 2, or 3; counseling available to engage the patient in treatment
		Necessary when the client is a danger to themselves or others because of medical and/or mental health issues
		Can also apply to medical detoxification (often required for people who are dependent on alcohol or other central nervous system depressants)
		This is typically a short stay (less than a week) and usually precedes either residential treatment or partial hospitalization
		Longer stays may be necessary when the client has a severe mental illness, if the client is unable to care for themselves (or remain safe), or in cases of protracted withdrawal symptoms requiring medical monitoring
Opioid treatment program	OTP	Daily or several times weekly opioid medication and counseling is available to maintain multidimensional stability for those with opioid use disorder

GOAL SETTING

Regardless of the level of treatment that a client requires, treatment should not be time-limited. The length of treatment should vary as a function of the severity of the client's illness and their response to treatment. The lengths of stay mentioned in the previous handout are listed as ranges of time for this reason—some clients will need more structured treatment than others. On the other hand, programs that offer fixed lengths of stay go against best practices that emphasize the importance of person-centered, outcomes-driven treatment (Mee-Lee et al., 2013).

In addition, treatment should be goal-focused, with goals determined by the client in consultation with the clinician. Goals are an important part of any treatment plan because they give focus to your interventions. To help clients accomplish their stated goals, it is helpful to break down goals into smaller steps or objectives. These objectives should be *measurable* (so you can track progress), *realistic* (so the client can achieve them), *flexible* (so the client can adjust them as needed), and *time-related* (so you can have a target date for completion). It is also important to include any specific people or agencies who will be helping the client with these objectives.

For example, if a client's goal is to stop using heroin, the following might be some sample objectives to include on their treatment plan:

> **Objective:** I will enroll in a Suboxone clinic and follow clinic guidelines (e.g., taking my medication as prescribed and attending groups).
>
> **Objective:** I will use heroin less than two times a week for the next month.
>
> **Objective:** I will attend four Narcotics Anonymous (or SMART Recovery) meetings per week.
>
> **Objective:** I will obtain Narcan to keep in the home and show the people I live with how to administer it should I overdose.
>
> **Timeframe:** I will accomplish these objectives within the next 30 days.

DRUG TESTING

As we saw in chapter 4, drug testing can be used to place a client in the correct level of treatment. It can also gauge a client's ongoing progress to sobriety in their current level of treatment. However, it should not be used punitively. Positive ("dirty") drug screens have historically been used to terminate clients from treatment, housing, or other services—meaning that if the client tests positive for substances, they are kicked out of the program. Unfortunately, punitive practices are still used in many settings—with the result being an increase in overdose deaths—but with guidance from ASAM and best practice models that consider SUD a chronic illness, this approach is changing. William White (2014), a pioneer in the field of addiction, said it best:

> There is no other major health problem for which one is admitted for professional care and then punitively discharged from treatment for becoming symptomatic in the service setting. For other health care problems, symptom manifestation serves as a confirmation of diagnosis or feedback that alternative methods of treatment and alternative approaches to patient education and motivation are needed. (p. 519)

Instead of terminating a client from services, a history of positive drug screens while in treatment, for either illicit or unprescribed substances, can mean the client is not currently receiving the correct treatment intensity.

A positive drug screen during treatment can also be a way to engage clients in conversation. The key for clinicians is to convey an honest and direct, but nonjudgmental, attitude toward their clients:

> **Clinician:** I am glad you chose to work on your recovery in our program, and I know you've been working hard.
>
> **Client:** Thanks.
>
> **Clinician:** I need to share with you that you tested positive on your last drug screen, and you told me that you had not used in three weeks. What's up?
>
> **Client:** Yeah, sorry 'bout that…
>
> **Clinician:** No need to apologize. What's going on?
>
> **Client:** I got into a fight with my girlfriend over the weekend, walked out, and found some coke as soon as I could so I'd feel better.
>
> **Clinician:** I appreciate you telling me that. Perhaps we can talk about those types of situations and the different ways to handle them, because they come up all the time.
>
> **Client:** Are you kicking me out?
>
> **Clinician:** No. Why?
>
> **Client:** Because I've been kicked out of programs before for pissing dirty, and I figured you'd do that too.
>
> **Clinician:** I can't see how kicking you out would be helpful.

Sometimes these conversations with clients don't go as smoothly, especially when clients are used to being defensive because of bad interactions they've had with providers in the past. As you will learn in chapter 7 in the context of MI, discussing drug screen results with clients can present an opportunity to roll with resistance. Here's an example of a conversation where the client is more defensive about their results. Notice how the clinician does not overreact and avoids a power struggle.

> **Clinician:** I need to share with you that you tested positive on your last drug screen, and you told me that you had not used in three weeks. What's up?
>
> **Client:** What are you accusing me of?
>
> **Clinician:** I'm not accusing you of anything, only sharing the results of the screen and how we can use that to help you in your recovery.
>
> **Client:** But I didn't use.
>
> **Clinician:** Our results suggest otherwise, so I'm not going to argue about it.
>
> **Client:** So you're kicking me out?
>
> **Clinician:** Nope. I just want to talk about this.

Client:	But I didn't use.
Clinician:	And I'm not going to argue about that. I just want to talk. You are not in trouble. We are not kicking you out. Just think it over.

My general preference is to avoid arguing for argument's sake. Is it possible this was false positive? Perhaps. If it was an error, then the issue will soon fade into memory. If it becomes a pattern, then you and your client will need to talk about what is not working in treatment and what you need to do differently, including whether or not the client would benefit from transitioning to a higher level of care.

PHARMACOTHERAPY FOR OPIOID USE DISORDER

Despite the fact that some treatment plans aim to have clients be completely "clean," the best course of action can sometimes be other medications. When I started working in SUD treatment, I had a negative view of pharmacotherapy, also called medication-assisted therapy. What sense did it make to give a person an opioid like methadone to get them to stop taking another opioid like heroin? As I spent more time in the field, read clinical literature, and worked with more clients, my opinions changed.

As of this writing, I work with a team that is expanding access to pharmacotherapy for clients with opioid use disorder in Virginia. When I am asked, "Aren't you just replacing one drug for another?" I quickly reply, "Yes I am." I then wait a moment because the person usually expects an argument. I continue with, "Yes, Suboxone is an opioid like heroin and fentanyl. But people prescribed Suboxone know what they are getting from the pharmacy, and when used as prescribed, it is safe. People buying drugs illicitly have no idea what they are getting, and the high death rates from overdose bear this out. People who are on medication for opioid use disorder have an opportunity to get better; people who are dead do not."

Medications like Suboxone and methadone work by keeping the client from experiencing opioid withdrawal symptoms (also called "dope sickness") while also blocking the euphoric effects should the client use heroin or another opioid, thus discouraging the client from continuing use. Both chemicals allow the brain to heal from opioid use and provide opportunities for the client to address the underlying causes of their SUD. On the next handout, you'll find more information about different types of medications used in opioid replacement therapy.

Although pharmacotherapy is very effective, there are often barriers to treatment, including stigma and concerns about diversion-related dangers (which are often unfounded). There are also not enough providers prescribing medications in addition to providing rigid program requirements including the following (Jakubowski & Fox, 2020):

- Abstinence is often a treatment goal (e.g., no positive UDS).

- Clients must attend counseling either before starting medication or to continue medication.

- Clients must attend outside peer support groups.

- Although behavioral health treatment is an important part of medication-assisted therapy, clients should not be forced to receive counseling to be able to receive pharmacotherapy.

Medications for Opioid Use Disorder

METHADONE

Pros	Cons
Has strong evidence suggesting its use for opioid use disorder is effective.	It is responsible for some opioid overdose deaths, especially when used with alcohol or benzodiazepines.
Chemically unlike heroin or morphine, so withdrawal develops more slowly.	Not readily available; It is delivered in liquid or pill form in opioid treatment programs, previously called methadone clinics. Many potential clients live far from clinics, while other clients have transportation difficulties.
Lasts 24–36 hours, allowing clients to work, attend school, parent, and engage in prosocial activities.	Although it is important to receive a sufficient dosage for methadone to be effective (at least 80 mg/day), many clients—especially non-White minorities—do not receive a high enough dose. This is likely due to the continued stigma of methadone, even within the broader SUD treatment and recovery community (Andraka-Christou, 2020).

BUPRENORPHINE

Pros	Cons
Buprenorphine causes less respiratory depression than methadone and has a ceiling effect at 32 mg, which makes overdose less likely, except when mixed with alcohol or benzodiazepines.	Should clients try to inject or insufflate the buccal or pill form of the drug, they will experience withdrawal symptoms, though people have found ways around this by chemically separating the naloxone, or they simply suffer through the withdrawal symptoms caused by the naloxone, which last about 20 to 30 minutes (Kavanaugh & McLean, 2020).
In 2017, the Food and Drug Administration approved Sublocade®, which is an injectable form of buprenorphine.	
Buprenorphine is an opioid agonist in low doses and an antagonist in high doses. When taken as prescribed, it is less likely to result in feelings of euphoria than methadone (Andraka-Christou, 2020).	

NALTREXONE AND NALOXONE

- These medications have antagonistic properties, meaning they will block the effects of opioids (naltrexone) or cause a person using opioids to go into withdrawal (naloxone).
- Naltrexone (Vivitrol®) is a deterrent that blocks the euphoric effects of opioids, cocaine, and alcohol and is used to prevent relapse by limiting cravings. Time-release injectable versions and implant versions are available.
- Naloxone (Narcan) is injected or used intra-nasally to reverse an opiate overdose.

WITHDRAWAL MANAGEMENT

There are no established medications or medical protocols to address withdrawal management (formerly called *detoxification*) from substances other than opioids, alcohol, or sedatives. In these cases, treatment should take a supportive approach by helping the client feel comfortable and safe; a quiet setting with peer support can be helpful. Certain symptoms may be managed medically, but it should be done carefully (e.g., the use of antipsychotic medications to address withdrawal-induced psychosis). In addition, while certain withdrawal symptoms may be primarily psychological, the cravings, depression, insomnia, and severe anxiety that clients may experience are profoundly disturbing and should not be minimized.

Withdrawal management alone is *not* treatment and is rarely successful without follow-up treatment and multidimensional support. As I've noted, SUD involves more than just using a drug; there are many things that lead to SUD, and these factors must be addressed for treatment to be effective. The ASAM goals for withdrawal management are as follows (Herron & Brennan, 2015):

1. To provide a safe withdrawal from the drug(s) of dependence and enable the patient to become drug-free

2. To provide a withdrawal that is humane and thus protects the patient's dignity

3. To prepare the patient for ongoing treatment of their dependence on alcohol or other drugs

The following handout provides some considerations for the pharmacological management of stimulant, alcohol (and other sedatives), and nicotine withdrawal.

Medication for Withdrawal Management

Stimulants	• There is currently no approved medication for the treatment of stimulant use disorder. • Several pilot studies show that bupropion, naltrexone, or topiramate may help people with methamphetamine use disorder, but more research is needed (Trivdei et al., 2021). • Short-acting benzodiazepines can be used to treat agitation or sleep disturbance, but they should be used cautiously due to their own dependence liability. • Persistent depression due to stimulant withdrawal syndrome may be treated with antidepressant medications.
Alcohol and other sedatives	• Benzodiazepines (and sometimes barbiturates) are used to help clients experiencing withdrawal from alcohol and other depressant medications. • These medications are usually administered within a withdrawal management plan (e.g., CIWA protocol). • Disulfiram (Antabuse) has been used as part of behavior modification for decades by discouraging drinking through negative feedback. • Disulfiram blocks the breakdown of acetaldehyde by acetaldehyde-dehydrogenase, leading to a concentration of the former. This leads to the person feeling nauseous if they ingest any alcohol (or even expose it on their skin). • The biggest issue with disulfiram is medication compliance. • Another medication used in alcohol treatment is naltrexone, though studies show mixed results in curbing alcohol cravings.
Nicotine	• Patches have been used as a form of nicotine replacement, including Nicotrol® and NicoDerm CQ®. • Most patches last 1 to 3 days, though they can take 6 hours to reach full effect. • Other nicotine products, such as gum, nasal spray, inhalers, and lozenges, work faster than a patch. • Chantix® is a non-nicotine medication used to help individuals quit smoking (although its side effects can discourage adherence). • Zyban® is actually the antidepressant Wellbutrin® marketed as a smoking cessation aid.

Inpatient Withdrawal Management

Impatient withdrawal management occurs in medical hospitals, psychiatric hospitals, and medically managed residential programs. The focus is on medical stability during detoxification. Methadone or buprenorphine are typically used to taper clients who are withdrawing from opioids, and they may be given clonidine, Zofran®, lofexidine, and other medications to help alleviate symptoms. Diazepam, lorazepam, chlordiazepoxide, or barbiturates are used to taper clients who are withdrawing from alcohol or other sedatives. Once the client is stable, they are transitioned to a less intense level of care, sometimes within the same facility (e.g., a residential or partial hospitalization program).

> The Clinical Institute Withdrawal Assessment for Alcohol Scale, Revised (CIWA-AR; Sullivan et al., 1989) and Clinical Opiate Withdrawal Scale (COWS; Wesson & Ling, 2003) are used in both outpatient and inpatient settings to measure signs and symptoms of withdrawal and guide appropriate symptom management. Both are available online.

Outpatient Withdrawal Management

Outpatient withdrawal management is provided in private clinics, community mental health centers, and outpatient drug treatment centers. Because of the risk of seizure and delirium, alcohol and benzodiazepine detoxification is typically conducted in an inpatient setting, while opioid withdrawal is typically managed on an outpatient basis.

Regardless of whether a client is receiving inpatient or outpatient treatment, they will most likely need some support with managing the symptoms of withdrawal. Determining their required level of care should be part of any ongoing assessment. ASAM outlines several levels of withdrawal management, as provided in the following handout.

ASAM Criteria Level of Withdrawal Management[*]

Level of Withdrawal Management	Level	Description
Ambulatory withdrawal management without extended on-site monitoring	1-WM	Mild withdrawal with daily or less-than-daily outpatient supervision; likely to complete withdrawal management and to continue treatment or recovery
Ambulatory withdrawal management with extended on-site monitoring	2-WM	Moderate withdrawal with all-day withdrawal management support and supervision; at night, has supportive family or living situation; likely to complete withdrawal management
Clinically managed residential withdrawal management	3.2-WM	Minimal to moderate withdrawal but needs 24-hour support to complete withdrawal management and to increase the likelihood of continuing treatment or recovery
Medically monitored inpatient withdrawal management	3.7-WM	Severe withdrawal and needs 24-hour nursing care and physician visits as necessary; unlikely to complete withdrawal management without medical and nursing monitoring
Medically managed inpatient withdrawal management	4-WM	Severe, unstable withdrawal and needs 24-hour nursing care and daily physician visits to modify the withdrawal management regimen and manage medical instability

[*] Used with permission from *The ASAM Essentials of Addiction Medicine, Third Edition* (Herron & Brennan, 2020).

Strategies to Improve Client Engagement

MOTIVATIONAL INTERVIEWING

Motivational interviewing (MI) developed out of a distaste for older, confrontational SUD treatment models. I witnessed this firsthand when I was an intern in a residential SUD treatment program. Confrontation, much of it personal, was everywhere. Clients were assumed to lie all the time, and "breaking them down" emotionally was deemed appropriate treatment. When I asked the staff why clients were treated this way, I was told: "That's how addiction treatment works." Much of it was simply bullying by staff and peers. As a result, many people walked out of treatment and resumed using. At the time, I wondered if there was a different way.

When I started working full-time in SUD treatment, I became trained in MI and found it to be a refreshing alternative to the confrontational styles of my former program. MI, a person-centered communication strategy, is made up of four core practices:

1. **Roll with resistance:** Instead of arguing with clients and trying to prove your point, you can accept that clients may be resistant. Frame their resistance outright instead of confronting it.

> **Client:** How are you supposed to help me?
>
> **Clinician:** You are concerned about my qualifications in being able to help you? That is okay. I am glad that you are thinking about how I can help you.

2. **Express empathy:** Be nice, accepting, and nonjudgmental—why not?

> **Client:** I can't believe that after three years of being sober, I started using again.
>
> **Clinician:** Returning to use can happen to anyone. It doesn't mean that what you learned before is no longer useful. The important thing is that you are here now; that takes courage.

3. **Develop discrepancy:** Help the client see where their current behaviors don't fit with their overall goals.

> **Client:**   All my friends go to the clubs and use, and I don't want to be alone, so I go with them.
>
> **Clinician:** Then what happens?
>
> **Client:**   I use cocaine, pills, whatever is there.
>
> **Clinician:** Well, you've talked about your plan to become independent again and get custody of your kids back. How does going to the club (and inevitably using) fit into this plan?

4. **Support self-efficacy:** Allow clients to make choices for themselves, including choices we may not like.

> **Client:**   I feel ready to stop using heroin, but I don't want to give up marijuana. Can I still be in this program?
>
> **Clinician:** Our program follows best practices that include individualized recovery plans. We believe there are risks associated with continued use of substances like cannabis, and I am happy to talk with you about that if you like, but we will work with you on the goals you choose.

You can practice doing MI by using OARS (open-ended questions, affirmations, reflections, summarizing) and by utilizing a decisional balance to explore the pros and cons of making a change versus maintaining the status quo.

The OARS of MI: Open-Ended Questions, Affirmations, Reflections, Summarizing

Open-Ended Questions

"How can I help you with _____?"

"What would you like to be different?"

"What made you decide to ask for help/work on this issue now?"

"What would happen if you didn't make any changes?"

"If you woke up tomorrow and _____ was no longer a problem for you, how would your life look?"

Affirmations

"You did a good job."

"I enjoyed talking with you today."

"That is a good suggestion."

"You have a lot of strengths."

"You showed up today. That's half the battle!"

Reflections

"So, you feel…."

"It sounds like you…."

"I can see how hard that was for you…"

"So, for you, it was…"

"In your eyes, the situation was…"

Summarizing

"Let me see if I understand so far…"

"Here's what I've heard. Tell me if I've missed anything."

"Let me take a pause here and make sure I understand…"

"I want to make sure I have this right…"

"This is important. You said…"

Decisional Balance Sheet

Every decision we make in life is associated with a particular outcome. This worksheet is designed to help you determine what the possible outcomes of making a decision or change in your life might be.

Think about an important change you want to make in your life and write it in the space below. Next, list out all the advantages (pros) of making this change, as well as the disadvantages (cons) of doing so. Then consider all the pros and cons of *not* changing. Take some time with this worksheet and consider keeping it with you to jot down ideas that may come to you over the next few days. Here's an example to get you started:

Change You Are Considering Making: _Stopping my use of alcohol_

Pros of Making the Change	Cons of Making the Change
I will feel better physically and emotionally. I will save money by not purchasing alcohol. I will not get sick or hungover as often. I will have more time to do other things I enjoy.	I might gain weight because I'll eat more instead of drinking. It might be harder to fall asleep without drinking before bed. I will not be able to have a drink when I feel angry or upset. I might lose friendships because many of my friends drink.
Pros of *Not* Making the Change	**Cons of *Not* Making the Change**
I don't like change; it's easier for me when things to stay the same. I like how alcohol tastes. I like getting drunk and how it feels. I enjoy spending time with my friends when we're drinking.	My spouse has told me she will leave if I don't stop drinking. My doctor has told me that heavy drinking is bad for my health. I may alienate myself from the people I love; I'm terrified of being alone.

Change You Are Considering Making: _____

Pros of Making the Change	Cons of Making the Change

Pros of *Not* Making the Change	Cons of *Not* Making the Change

Steps Toward Change

Big changes begin with little changes. Even the smallest, most seemingly inconsequential change can have big implications. Sometimes having a plan to start making these small changes can be helpful. Use the following questions to help you develop that plan.

What is something you want to change? (Think big.)

What are three smaller changes you can make now that might help you work toward the big change you would like to make?

What has worked in the past when you tried to make these changes?

What has not worked when you tried to make these changes?

Who are some people who can help you make these changes?

What are some other things that can help you make these changes?

STAGES OF CHANGE MODEL

MI is based on Prochaska and DiClemente's (Prochaska & Velicer, 1997) Transtheoretical Model of behavioral change, which is sometimes called the Stages of Change Model. This model, made up of six separate stages, can be used for any type of behavioral change in a person. The multistep model shows that changing a behavior is a process and that habits and actions are rarely altered on a whim. The following graphic shows the most common order, but I have found that people can go from stage to stage in any order.

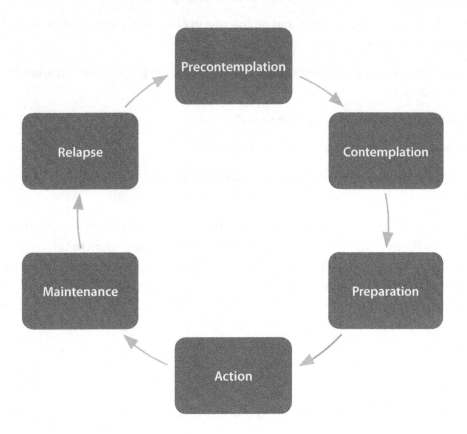

Precontemplation

- The person may be unaware of any reasons for changing: "Problem? What problem?"

- They may resist being told what to do or rationalize why they do not need to change.

- They may feel hopeless about ever changing or have given up any desire to change.

- They may need the opportunity to learn and reflect on their behavior's impact on their life.

Many clinicians find working with clients in the precontemplation stage to be the most challenging and may even find it easy to give up. You may find yourself wondering if you're in the movie *Groundhog Day*, reliving the same conversation over and over. The first thing to remember is that we as clinicians cannot force anyone to change. Focus instead on what the client believes that they get from their actions. Often therapists ask, "How is that working for you?" This should not be communicated in a cynical way, but matter of fact. Remember that people begin to consider changing when the benefits of potential change outweigh the costs of not changing.

Contemplation

- The client recognizes that there is a problem, but they are either ambivalent about making changes or are not committed to changing currently.

- People in this stage are usually open to collecting information about the behavior and weighing the pros and cons of changing or not changing.

- Remember that just because a client has an interest in changing does not mean that they are ready to do so at this time.

- At this stage, pay attention to change statements that may signify a client's readiness to move into the next stage:

    - "My use has gotten out of hand at times."

    - "If I don't stop, something bad is going to happen."

    - "I'm going to do something, I'm just not sure what."

It can be difficult to determine when a client transitions from precontemplation to contemplation, and clients often vacillate between the two stages. Clinician encouragement is very important in this stage, and this is usually easier because, by this time, a relationship has developed with the client. An important thing to remember in this stage is that when the client is ready to move to the next stage, you must move with them. I have seen clinicians spend a lot of time summarizing and reflecting client statements back to the client when the client is clearly ready to move forward.

Preparation

- The client has accepted the idea of making changes and begins to look at ways to start.

- This can involve attempting to decrease the amount of use or setting a date to stop using.

- The client may begin to change other things in their life that could support the main change, such as attending 12-step support groups, researching possible treatment interventions, or engaging in positive activities not directly related to their SUD (e.g., obtaining housing or employment).

This is a big shift—from thinking alone to beginning to act. It is important that clinicians have the resources to help the client gather anything needed to make this change. It is equally important that clinicians balance their encouragement of the client with patience and knowledge that putting a plan into action takes time. You may have frustrations or impatience—these are understandable. Clinicians are human and we want what's best for our clients. When you do feel this way, do not let it be interpreted by the client that they are not moving fast enough or they may return to precontemplation or leave treatment entirely.

Action

> - The client takes a definitive step to make changes in their life, like entering treatment.
> - This can also include working a 12-step program instead of just passively attending the group.

When I first learned about the Stages of Change Model, I saw the action stage as a client going "somewhere," usually residential treatment. Since most clients do not go to residential treatment, this is not the only way that clients can move into the action phase. This is a transition for the counselor to move from the Stages of Change Model to a more formalized SUD treatment, like cognitive behavioral therapy (CBT) or other approaches. It is very important to keep in mind that clients may act on some aspects of their problem while remaining in an earlier stage of change regarding another aspect of their problem.

Several years ago, I was working with a young woman, Paula, who came to our clinic for opioid use disorder. Her boyfriend accompanied her. Both were started on Suboxone, but the boyfriend stopped coming to treatment after a week while Paula continued. She quickly engaged in group therapy and stabilized on the medication, but she also realized that her boyfriend, with whom she lived, did not want to stop using heroin. Paula began the process of recognizing that remaining with her boyfriend was untenable in the long term, but fully severing physical, emotional, and financial ties with him took a great deal of time. Paula did eventually leave her boyfriend, but she could only do this after months of preparation, knowing she could live safely and independently.

Maintenance

> - The client works to maintain the gains that they have made and prevent lapses to earlier stages.
> - Clients at this stage acknowledge that lapses can occur and continuously develop strategies to address potential lapses (e.g., being a sponsor).

Maintenance can be seen as an indefinite stage but should not be viewed by the client as a time where they can "just coast along." This could be a time for the client to address other areas in their lives. Some clients use the maintenance stage to help others in their recovery, a principle long-supported by the 12-step movement.

Relapse

> - The client slips back into previous patterns of behavior and begins using substances again.
> - A *relapse* is defined as a return to *regular* use after a period of sobriety (different from a *lapse*, which involves a limited period of use without a return to regular use).
> - Some of the determinates of relapse include the client's degree of self-efficacy, motivation, coping skills, and quality and size of their social support system.
> - Given that relapse is often a part of SUD, part of treatment is to anticipate relapses, develop ways to both avoid them and manage them if they happen, and minimize their potential harm.

Relapse Prevention Strategies*

1. Help clients understand relapse as both a process and event, and help them learn to identify their warning signs for relapse, which can include:

    *   Exhibiting attitudinal, emotional, cognitive, and behavioral changes (e.g., increased frustrations with everyday things, thinking more about using, justifying use, decreasing use of previously helpful relapse prevention strategies).

    *   Reducing contact with helpful peers.

2. Help clients identify their high-risk situations and develop effective cognitive and behavioral coping strategies.

    *   Relapses are usually the result of a series of small, *apparently irrelevant* decisions that may appear to have nothing to do with substance use, but, in a small way, move the client closer to returning to use (e.g., start hanging out with people who are not supportive of one's recovery, decreasing activities that have helped with recovery, adding a lot of things in one's life that increase overall stress).

3. Help clients enhance their communication skills, cultivate interpersonal relationships, and develop a recovery social network.

    *   Involving family members and social supports in treatment enhances the client's recovery efforts.

    *   Engaging in peer or mutual support groups is also helpful.

4. Help clients identify , manage and reduce uncomfortable or distressing emotions that may trigger a relapse.

    *   Encourage individuals to change their behaviors relative to a certain emotional state (e.g., exercise when depressed).

5. Help clients identify and manage cravings and cues that precede cravings (e.g., "How do you identify a thought or feeling as a craving?").

    *   Work with the client to help them understand that cravings do not last forever and that they can talk themselves through the cravings (e.g., "I know this is a thought [or feeling]. My thoughts and feelings do not control me. I do not need to act upon them. They will pass.")

6. Challenge the client's *euphoric recall* (i.e., their tendency to only remember the good things that come with using) by highlighting the negative consequences of use (e.g., keep a list of potential consequences and add to it as you think of additional items).

---

* Used with permission from *The ASAM Essentials of Addiction Medicine, Third Edition* (Herron & Brennan, 2020).

7. Help clients identify cognitive distortions and use counterthoughts to challenge these distortions.

   • Example: A client who thinks "I'll die if I don't use" can learn to challenge this distortion with the (more realistic) counter-thought "There's a greater chance that I'll die from an overdose if I continue to use."

8. Help clients work toward a more balanced lifestyle.

   • Recovery is more than being sober. Explore each area of the client's life, including one's physical health, mental well-being, spirituality, and relationships with others, and determine where support can be added.

   • Consider the use of medications in combination with psychosocial treatments.

   • Facilitate the transition between levels of care for individuals completing residential treatment, hospital-based inpatient treatment, partial hospitalization, or intensive outpatient programs.

   • Incorporate additional strategies to improve adherence to treatment and medications, such as MI.

Your Relapse Triggers

Relapse is not uncommon in people living with SUD. A big part of working toward recovery is understanding things that can lead to relapse. The following are some common triggers for relapse:

- **HALT** (hungry, angry, lonely, tired)
- **RIID** (restless, irritable, isolated, discontent)
- **BAAD** (bored, anxious, angry, depressed)

Use the following questions to help you understand the triggers for a possible relapse.

What are your triggers?

Why do you think these are triggers for you?

What are some things you can do differently, even if only for five minutes? (Sometimes waiting even five minutes before doing anything can help you make better decisions.)

Understanding Your Relapse

Relapses (or returning to use) happen. This does not mean you are a failure or that treatment does not work. Treatment is cumulative—even if you return to use, what you've learned before is often useful. Use the following questions to help you learn from your relapse.

Tell me about your most recent relapse. What happened?

How did you recognize that you had relapsed?

What does that relapse (or other peoples' relapses) mean to you?

How do you think about yourself during or following a relapse?

How do you think others think about you (or how do they treat you) following a relapse?

What are some things you can do to reduce the chance of a relapse?

Does Your Environment Support Your Recovery?

As you work toward your goals, take time to consider that there are a myriad of factors that can help or limit your recovery. Remember that some things can do both. It is important to be aware of these factors as you go through treatment. Use the following chart to learn how different parts of your life affect your recovery. Examples of how to begin a conversation for each factor are included; please note the examples may be contradictory.

Factors	How it Helps Recovery	How it Limits Recovery
Spouse/ Partner	My spouse does not have SUD.	My spouse does not understand (or accept) my SUD.
Children	I want to be the best parent I can be.	My children resent me because of my SUD, which makes me want to use even more.

Factors	How it Helps Recovery	How it Limits Recovery
Other Family Members	I have family members who are in recovery and who are supportive.	I'm outcast from my family because they view SUD as a moral failing on my part.
Living Environment	There are no substances in my home.	At least one other person in my home uses substances.
Work/School Environment	I enjoy my job and it gives me a sense of purpose.	I can't hold down a job.

Factors	How it Helps Recovery	How it Limits Recovery
Spiritual Practices	My faith helps sustain me.	My experiences with religion have not been helpful.
Other		

More Motivational Interviewing Strategies

1. **Change talk.** Frame all client statements in terms of making changes. I also focus on the client's ability to make choices.

> **Clinician:** Thank you for coming in.
>
> **Client:** Like I had a choice. Stupid judge ordered me to.
>
> **Clinician:** Still, you chose to come in.
>
> **Client:** Didn't you hear me? Either I come in to see you or I go to jail.
>
> **Clinician:** Would you believe that I've had some people choose not to come in and go to jail instead?
>
> **Client:** That's a stupid choice!
>
> **Clinician:** Agreed. That's why I'm glad you are here.

2. **Optimism for change.** Sometimes believing in a person's ability to change can be an impetus for them to realize they can change.

> **Client:** This is a waste of time!
>
> **Clinician:** What's a waste of time?
>
> **Client:** Coming here…treatment…trying to get clean…I can't do it.
>
> **Clinician:** The fact that you've showed up three times to meet with me shows that you want something better for yourself. I believe that you can change. It will take time, but I know you can do this.

3. **Normalizing.** When clients are so focused on a single problem, other areas of life can also appear to be problems when they really are not.

> **Client:** I've been working so hard on my recovery, but I still feel like a failure. Yesterday, my daughter came home with green hair!
>
> **Clinician:** Remind me again, how old is your daughter?

Client:	15.
Clinician:	I know it can be upsetting, but isn't a normal part of being 15 years old experimenting with how you look? Sounds like that's what happening here.

4. **Columbo approach.** If you are not familiar with this fictional detective played by Peter Falk, check him out. Columbo's strategy was to play dumb with a suspect and allow the person to give him the information he needed to solve the crime. This can work in counseling by providing opportunities for the client to explain their position, which in turn, can lead to further discussion (using the OARS questions).

Clinician:	Can you help me understand something? You've been working hard on not using, and you said that being around your ex-partner is a huge trigger?
Client:	Yeah, that's right.
Clinician:	Well, in talking about your weekend, you mentioned that you saw your ex, right?
Client:	[reluctantly] Yes…
Clinician:	So, if you want to stop using, how does hanging out with your ex help you work toward your goal?

5. **Supporting self-confidence.** Some clients need positive coaching as part of the counseling process, especially when learning ways to make decisions for themselves.

Client:	I wonder if I can do this.
Clinician:	Do what?
Client:	Sobriety, recovery, whatever you call it.
Clinician:	Are you wondering if you have the strengths and capacity to get better?
Client:	That sounds right.
Clinician:	Well, for starters, you're here and you keep showing up to treatment. And whether you see it or not, I see you improving. I know you can do this. It will take time, but we're with you.

6. **Readiness to change scale.** Using this scale can increase change talk as clients identify their motivations for changing.

> **Clinician:** On a scale of 1 to 10, with 10 being very ready and 1 being not ready at all, how would you rate your desire to change?
>
> **Client:** Probably a 3.
>
> **Clinician:** And why did you choose a 3 instead of a 2? Why didn't you choose a lower number?
>
> **Client:** I want to change more than I did last week, which I think was a 2.
>
> **Clinician:** Ok, so what happened this past week to move from a 2 to a 3? How can you get to a 4 next week?

7. **Therapeutic paradox.** This strategy includes siding with the option of maintaining the status quo, which will often get clients to argue back about the importance of change. It can also help you uncover any roadblocks getting in the way of change.

> **Clinician:** You've talked about making changes to your alcohol use but are still drinking every night. Maybe now is not the right time for you to try cutting back.
>
> **Client:** No, I want to try now. It's just hard to resist the cravings.
>
> **Clinician:** I hear you. Let's look at some things you've done to resist those cravings that worked and things that need work.

Looking to the Future and Dreaming Big

Acknowledging your past experiences is important, and so is looking ahead. I challenge you to see beyond your SUD and imagine where you want to be. This can include your treatment progress with SUD as well as other areas of your life, all of which are part of your overall recovery. Use the following questions to envision your future. Remember to be as specific as possible.

Where do you want to be in…

1 month?

6 months?

1 year?

5 years?

10 years?

What are three things you can begin doing today to begin to make these dreams realities?

CONTINGENCY MANAGEMENT

Contingency management is a well-studied behavioral intervention that rewards positive or desired behaviors with nominal rewards, such as gift cards or vouchers that increase in value the longer the client continues the desired behavior. Some examples of positive behaviors you might want to reinforce include negative drug screens and participation in treatment.

The Impact of Contingency Management

- Improves treatment retention
- Incentivizes clients to continue receiving services along the continuum of care
- Reduces drug consumption
- Fosters a supportive environment within a group treatment setting

However, when using contingency management, it's important for the rewards to have some value for the client, or they won't be motivated to sustain the behavior change. About half of people who engage in contingency management tend to respond quickly, while the other half do not respond at all. The following handout provides an example of a contingency management developed by my coworker in our opioid treatment program.

A Contingency Management Example[*]

Clients meet with a prescriber and then attend a treatment group once per week. Every client receives candy and encouragement for participating in the program that day. Clients can receive additional rewards for meeting the following criteria:

- Arriving on time for group and submitting a drug screen

- Having a negative drug screen (no illicit drugs or non-prescribed substances)

- Testing positive for buprenorphine (demonstrates adherence to medication for opioid use disorder)

Clients who meet all the above criteria are eligible to draw a small slip of paper from a fishbowl that has prize identifiers. Clients who earn a prize have the chance to pick from prizes within the price range printed on their slip of paper. The following are the odds of winning different prizes:

- 48% receive a motivational quote on the back and an additional piece of candy.

- 40% receive a small prize option ($5); clients pick their reward.

- 10% receive a large prize option ($10); clients pick their reward.

- 2% receive a jumbo prize ($20); clients pick their reward.

_____
[*] Used with permission from Adam Creveling, MSW.

CARE COORDINATION AND RECOVERY CAPITAL

Care coordination, sometimes called case management, recognizes that treatment involves more than addressing a client's substance use, and it helps clients link to services in the community while reducing barriers to recovery. Quality care coordination does not perform tasks for clients that they are able to do for themselves; rather, it informs and empowers clients to connect with needed resources (Center for Substance Abuse Treatment [CSAT], 2000). The following are items or services your client may need to assist them in their recovery work:

- Securing housing
- Obtaining food vouchers
- Access to food pantries
- Medical treatment
- Mental health counseling
- Psychiatric care
- Obtaining health insurance
- Dental care
- Transportation
- Childcare

- Job searches
- Enrolling in job training
- Financial assistance
- Clothing
- Enrolling in adult education
- Enrolling children in school
- Immigration services
- Meeting legal system obligations (e.g., coordinating with probation or parole)

Why Is Care Coordination So Important in SUD Treatment?

- Retention in treatment is associated with better outcomes, and a principal goal of care coordination is to keep clients engaged in treatment and moving toward recovery.

- Treatment may be more likely to succeed when a client's other problems are addressed concurrently with substance use.

- Comprehensive SUD treatment often requires that clients move to different levels of care or systems, and case coordination facilitates such movement (CSAT, 2000).

Recovery capital refers to the resources that clients have that can support their recovery. Clients and the communities in which they live have varying amounts of recovery capital. For example, clients with high personal recovery capital may work, have a home, and be physically healthy, while those with low personal recovery capital may be unemployed, lack housing, and have medical concerns that need to be addressed as part of their recovery. Similarly, clients with high family/social recovery capital have people in their lives who can provide support in the form of material resources and encouragement, while those with low family/social recovery capital may not have such assistance. Finally, those with high community recovery capital have access to needed resources in their environment like childcare or employee assistance programs, while those with low recovery capital in this area do not.

Personal
Recovery Capital:
The client's emotional
well-being, physical health,
safety, and access to
housing, income, health
insurance, and food

Community
Recovery Capital:
Resources available in
the client's community, such
as health care, childcare,
transportation, and housing

Family/Social
Recovery Capital:
The resources and support
available to the client from
their family and friends, such
as emotional or financial
support and help with
childcare or transportation

PEER RECOVERY

Peer-based recovery was a component of SUD treatment long before the founding of AA (White, 2014). A peer recovery specialist is someone with lived experience when it comes to mental health issues or SUD and who is trained to support others working through their own recovery. There are differing qualifying criteria to become a peer specialist across states, but it is widely accepted that a peer with shared experiences can engage and sustain others in treatment. I will address the specific role of peer recovery specialists in the following handout.

As treatment programs move away from a strictly medical model toward recovery-based models, peer recovery specialists are an integral part of this transformation. You can find certified peer specialists in many settings, including (but not limited to) treatment centers, emergency departments, and prisons and jails.

What Is a Peer Recovery Specialist?

A peer recovery specialist is someone who has walked their path to recovery from substance use or mental illness and is now helping others walk their own path.

What Peer Recovery Specialists Do

- Talk with you about the similar circumstances they have experienced

- Help you understand recovery and the treatment process

- Reduce stigma

- Connect you with peer services in the community

- Assist you in understanding how their agency works

- Facilitate peer-led groups (groups in which clinicians are not present, only peers!)

- Provide harm reduction resources

- Connect you with other peers

What Peer Recovery Specialists Do Not Do

- Provide therapy

- Engage in inappropriate relationships with clients (that means no dating or spending time together outside of peer recovery activities)

- Provide money to clients

CLIENT TERMINATION

Since clients determine what recovery means to them, clients with SUD often determine when their treatment is complete. Like many clients, those with SUD may self-terminate by simply not coming to treatment any longer. Hopefully, you can have a planned termination, but regardless of how treatment ends, I believe that the door should be left open for clients to return should they need it. As I have stated before, it is not unusual for clients to stop and restart treatment several times.

When working with clients with SUD, only rarely should you terminate a client in the middle of treatment. If your client is continuing to use substances, this may indicate a need for a higher level of care and is not a reason to end treatment. There are times, however, when termination is warranted. If a client becomes violent, or threatens violence, toward peers or staff, this is grounds for dismissal. But in my experience, this is generally an uncommon occurrence. Of the more than 300 clients who were admitted to an office-based opioid treatment program I managed several years ago, only one person was terminated for this reason. Distributing illicit substances on clinic property is another reason for termination, as it places other people in the program, and the program itself, in danger.

Individual Cognitive Behavioral Therapy

COGNITIVE BEHAVIORAL THERAPY

Although various clinical modalities are used to treat SUD, CBT represents one of the most used approaches. Similar forms of therapy, such as rational-emotive behavioral therapy (REBT) and dialectical behavioral therapy (DBT), have their roots in CBT—one could also argue that CBT is rooted in REBT—but in this chapter I am going to focus on CBT. I also want to be clear that CBT is not the only approach to treat SUD in individual therapy. Psychodynamic approaches, which can include object relations therapy, ego psychology, and internal family systems therapy, can also be effective. I am focusing on CBT because it provides a structured approach to counseling that can be used with clients who continue to struggle with SUD, as well those as who are well into their recovery.

CBT is based on the notion that how we think influences how we feel and behave. A fundamental component of the cognitive behavioral framework is the ABC model:

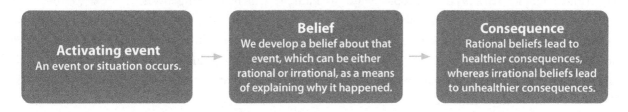

Activating event
An event or situation occurs.

Belief
We develop a belief about that event, which can be either rational or irrational, as a means of explaining why it happened.

Consequence
Rational beliefs lead to healthier consequences, whereas irrational beliefs lead to unhealthier consequences.

The ABC model holds that events themselves do not cause our emotions. Rather, it is our *beliefs* or *interpretations* of those events that result in how we feel. Therefore, the goal of CBT is to help clients examine, interpret, and challenge any irrational beliefs, which results in a subsequent change to their emotions and behaviors.

THE COGNITIVE MODEL OF SUBSTANCE USE

When it comes to substance use, CBT treats SUD as a learned behavior that can be modified by targeting the underlying belief systems that drive substance use behavior. This approach is based on the cognitive model of substance use, which outlines a multistep process in which continued use or relapse occurs (Wright et al., 1993):

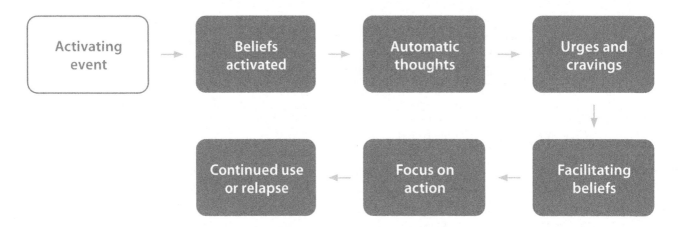

The model begins with an **activating event**, which can be a single event or a series of events, that trigger substance-related thoughts. This event can be innocuous and have nothing to do with substance use, but the key is that it begins the thinking process that could lead to substance use. For example, a client's spouse might muse, "I could really use some time to myself right now." This activating event directly triggers the person's initial **beliefs**, which are deeply engrained and typically skewed toward the negative. For example, after hearing their spouse request some time to themselves, the client may irrationally conclude, "They want time to themselves because I am a horrible partner," "I always drive people away," or "I am not worthy of being loved."

Our **automatic thoughts** flow directly from our beliefs, and we tend to be more aware of these thoughts when compared to our initial beliefs. These thoughts are often a reaction to our initial beliefs and may serve to relieve tension from those beliefs. Continuing with our example, the client might think, "I just want to have a drink" or "I'm going to get high." Again, this may be the first part of the process that the client is consciously aware of, but it is still being driven by those initial beliefs.

As the client becomes aware of their thoughts, they begin to have **physical cravings** and **emotional urges** to engage in behaviors connected to what they are thinking about. The client may think about walking into a bar, imagine tasting alcohol, or obsess over feeling high, numb, or relaxed. These cravings and urges then lead to **facilitating beliefs** that encourage substance use. This is an important step in the model because it is where the client attempts to justify their urges and cravings. In our example, the client's facilitating belief might be "Yeah, I deserve a drink." The essence of CBT is to recognize this process and then try something different. The goal is to help the client to believe "I know that using won't help me" or "I know these urges and cravings won't last forever."

Once a client develops a facilitating belief, they begin to focus on action. For example, the person might call their dealer to purchase drugs or drive to the corner store to purchase alcohol. This then leads to **continued use** or a **return to use**. The hope is that clients do not get to this stage, as your work in CBT is to limit the opportunities for this to occur.

In order to intervene at each stage of the model and help clients address the problems that often precipitate their SUD, CBT targets five areas:

1. **Managing cravings:** An important part of treatment involves helping clients understand that cravings are a substantial part of SUD. CBT can help them learn how to recognize cravings, how they experience cravings, and how to deal with their cravings.

2. **Avoiding high-risk situations:** Another important part of recovery involves avoiding situations where substances are available, as well as staying away from emotionally charged interactions that could trigger use.

3. **Case management:** The provision of case management helps clients connect with other services they may need that can support their journey toward recovery.

4. **Mood regulation:** With CBT, clients develop a better understanding of their feelings and how these feelings impact their thoughts. It also helps them see how substances are often used to change how they think and feel, and this can help teach them how to regulate their feelings without substances.

5. **Lifestyle changes:** SUD impacts the whole person, so treating SUD involves examining every aspect of a client's life, seeing all the things that impact their SUD, and making appropriate changes to support recovery.

To help your clients apply the cognitive model of substance use to their own lives, use the following worksheet, which details the steps involved in the cognitive model of substance use. This is followed by tools you can use to help your clients intervene at various points in the model and move in a different direction.

Applying the Cognitive Model of Substance Use

For each step in the cognitive model, think of some examples in your own life that moved you closer to use or caused you to return to use. Examples are provided for you first, followed by space for you to write in your own answers.

Activating Event:	Beliefs Activated:
I had a fight with my spouse. I am unable to find a job. I am feeling depressed.	"I sure could use a drink (or a shot, or a line) right now because it will make me feel better." "I'm a piece of crap anyway, so what's the point?" "I feel better when I'm high."
Automatic Thoughts:	**Urges and Cravings:**
"I deserve this." "I should just have a drink—it doesn't matter anyway."	I visualize myself sitting at the bar. I am thinking about how to get ahold of my substance of choice.
Facilitating Beliefs:	**Focus on Action:**
"This will be the last time, I promise." "I'll kick it tomorrow." "Drugs are the only things that make life worth living, and you only live once."	I go out to purchase alcohol or other substances. I go somewhere that drugs or alcohol are available. I hang out with people who use.

Continued use or return to use

Activating Event:	Beliefs Activated:

Automatic Thoughts:	Urges and Cravings:

Facilitating Beliefs:	Focus on Action:

WORKING THROUGH THE COGNITIVE MODEL OF SUBSTANCE USE

The first step in working through the cognitive model of substance use is to help your client identify their automatic thoughts. These automatic thoughts are often based on negative schemas, which are beliefs the client holds about themselves that are usually not true. Therefore, one initial treatment goal is for clients to be able to step back and ask themselves: "What am I thinking right now?" Clinicians can help clients work toward this goal by carefully listening for clues that arise in the course of conversation. To help illustrate this process, consider the following example with a client named Robert.

Robert: My wife left me shortly after she finished her degree. I can understand why.

Clinician: What do you mean "I can understand why"?

Robert: I mean, who can blame her for leaving?

Clinician: Something happened?

Robert: Not really. I just mean, who would want to stay with me?

Clinician: Why wouldn't she want to stay with you?

Robert: Because I'm a piece of crap.

Clinician: What makes you say that?

Robert: It's what I've always thought. It's what my parents told me.

Clinician: Your parents told you that you were a piece of crap?

Robert: When I screwed up, they told me that.

For Robert, it soon becomes apparent that he blames himself whenever others reject or hurt him. In his mind, it is always his fault, and he must have done something wrong. Notice that up until this point, the clinician is only helping Robert identify the automatic thought (which itself has nothing to do with substance use), not challenge the veracity of the thought. Once the clinician has helped Robert identify his automatic thoughts, he can help Robert question if these thoughts are true.

Clinician: So every time you made a mistake, your folks told you that you were a piece of crap?

Robert: Yeah. And just so you know, I'm talking about my mom and stepfather.

Clinician: These are the folks who raised you?

Robert: That's right.

Clinician: When you say, "screw up," what do you mean?

Robert: Bad grades, not making the baseball team, fighting, forgetting to take out the garbage, or the dog making a mess in the house.

Clinician: Hold on. Not all of those are your fault, and even then, calling you a piece of crap is wrong regardless.

Robert: Well, that's what they did.

Clinician: I believe what you're telling me. My question is, do you believe what they told you? That you are a piece of crap?

Robert: Well yeah, I'm always screwing up…

Clinician: But that doesn't make you a piece of crap. We all make mistakes.

Robert: *[Thinks this over for a minute]* I guess you're right.

Clinician: So can we explore the idea that you can make a mistake, and not automatically assume that you are a piece of crap?

This helps the client to move toward seeing himself more realistically and allows him to see situations differently.

Clinician: We started this conversation by discussing how sad you felt when your wife left you. What made you bring this up?

Robert: Since I stopped drinking as much, I've had a clearer head and have had time to think about her leaving.

Clinician: How many years ago did she leave?

Robert: Three.

Clinician: You were obviously sad when she left, and you blame yourself for this?

Robert: We were both drinking and drugging at the time, but yeah, it was on me.

Clinician: So, she has no responsibility? She had nothing to do with her choices?

Robert: Well, I was using.

Clinician: I am glad you've said twice now that your use played a part of what happened, but I want to emphasize that she made a decision for herself.

Robert: Because of me.

Clinician: But she chose to leave, perhaps due to your drug use or hers, as she was using too. As I've said before, the problems we have do not need to completely define us, so is it possible that while you have problems with substances, you are not a piece of crap?

After challenging Robert's negative automatic thought ("I'm a piece of crap") and encouraging him to develop alternative ways of seeing the situation ("I can make mistakes without being a piece of crap"), the clinician can then tie this to substance use.

Robert: I guess I never thought about it like that.

Clinician: Sure. And while you are not a piece of crap, we can still take a look at what you do when you feel that way. For example, when you feel like crap, what usually happens?

Robert: I like to escape, usually by getting high. When I was a teenager, I'd steal one of my stepdad's beers. He drank so much that he never missed it. I drank more as a I got older.

Clinician: Did you ever drink when you didn't feel like crap?

Robert: Sure, but not as much as when I felt like crap.

Clinician: Or when were told you were a piece of crap?

Robert: Yeah.

Clinician: So every time you felt like crap…

Robert: … I drank.

Clinician: Kind of an automatic thing—feeling like crap leads to drinking?

Robert: Yeah. Later it involved cocaine and pills. I'd use the coke to get the energy and pills and booze to come down.

Clinician: Almost seems automatic—you feel bad about something, blame yourself because you assume you're a piece of crap, then you use to forget or numb yourself.

Robert: Yeah, that sounds right. The next day I'd be hungover or exhausted and then I'd feel bad about using, so I'd again think that I was crap…

Clinician: That's a vicious cycle.

Robert: Right!

At this point, the clinician can work with Robert to develop additional strategies to replace his old habits (substance use) with new ones. However, helping Robert change his automatic thoughts and initial beliefs will take time, so it is likely that conversations like this will occur many times. Robert has a lot of work to do to reprogram his self-identity as someone more than what his folks labeled him as.

Clinician: What could you do differently when you feel like crap or something bad happens to you?

Robert: You mean instead of using?

Clinician: Yeah.

Robert: Sometimes I just go for a walk, and make sure I don't go near any of the places I used to drink.

Clinician: That's a good one, what else?

One tool that I have found is surprisingly effective when it comes to replacing old habits is reminder cards. When I first heard about them, I thought they would be useless. But many of my clients found them useful, with some even rewarding themselves with candy when they were able to resist the urge to use. You can simply have your clients write the following on an index card and keep it with them:

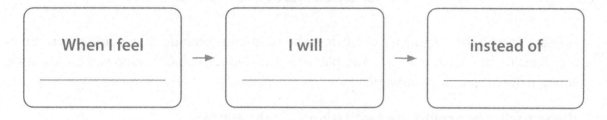

The following worksheet is also a helpful tool to help clients interrupt the pathway to substance use.

Changing Your Pathway to Substance Use

For each step in the cognitive model, describe what you could do that would move you in the direction of recovery. Some examples are provided for you first, followed by space for you to write in your own answers.

Use self-talk when confronted with triggering situations:

"I make bad decisions when I am angry."

"I am vulnerable when I feel strong emotions."

Question the accuracy of the initial belief:

• Ask yourself: "Is what I'm thinking true?"

Find ways to challenge automatic thoughts:

- Use reminder prompts to suggest other options:

  When I feel _____, I will _____ instead of _____.

- Challenge the thoughts:

  Although I really want to use right now, there are other things I can do to reward myself.

Manage urges and cravings:

- Remind yourself these are temporary. Wait five minutes before doing anything.
- Distract yourself.

Question the accuracy of the facilitating belief:

- Again, ask yourself: "Is what I am thinking true?"

Focus on taking nonsubstance-related action:

- Go to a group meeting.
- Call your sponsor.
- Go for a walk where you know there will not be triggers for you to use.

Continued recovery!

9

Substance Use Disorders and the Family

SUD is often called a family illness, because as one member's SUD affects the other members of the family, the family dynamics are simultaneously affecting the SUD. For this reason, it is not uncommon for more than one person in a family to be using substances. Given that the effects of substance use are interwoven in the family's dynamics, treatment can have a positive impact on the family system as a whole. However, to effectively engage the family in treatment, we first need to understand how family structures emerge in response to SUD.

WORKING WITH FAMILIES

When working with a family or a couple, it is imperative to remember that the family (not the individual) is the client. This is one of the primary reasons why clinicians who provide family or couples therapy don't treat members of each dyad or family in individual therapy. Doing so can cause unintentional alliances to form between specific family members and the clinician (or it can create the perception of such alliances, which can be equally damaging). When I provide family therapy, there are times during the assessment phase of counseling when I will speak with each family member separately, but I remind them that this is in the context of gathering information and that the family as a whole is my client.

Families, like most human systems, attempt to maintain a sense of balance or homeostasis. In general, people become used to how things are and inherently resist any attempts to make changes, even if it may be for the better. For some families, a drive toward homeostasis may be stronger than the desire for healing (Boyle et al., 2009). Clinicians need to understand this reality when working with families and remember that one of the key components of MI involves rolling with resistance when it presents itself. Remember, too, that society's definition of *family* is always changing, and how we define family today may include more than just individuals with whom we share biology or with whom we enter into marital, legal, or financial agreements. For many, the notion of family can also involve those we choose to surround ourselves with.

CONCEPTS OF PRACTICE

When working with families impacted by SUD, the concept of enabling often comes up in therapy. At its core, *enabling* occurs when a family member or friend does something for the person with SUD that they should do for themselves. In doing so, the enabler (for lack of a better word) shields the person with SUD from the consequences of their use. Enablers can be supportive when they minimize their own needs in favor of "rescuing" the person with SUD, or they can be hostile if they are disrespectful and aggressive, thereby increasing shame in the person with SUD (Herron & Brennan, 2015). The word *codependence* is often associated with the concept of enabling, as someone who is codependent can become emotionally, socially, and even physically "addicted to" the person with SUD, causing themselves to engage in enabling behaviors that allow the substance use to occur.

I think we need to be careful with the terms *enabling* and *codependency*. Some people believe that providing any help to a person with SUD is enabling. They may judge and shame other families, usually with the moniker of being "codependent," when they are merely trying to help (Avery & Avery, 2019; Szalavitz, 2021). Individuals with this shaming mindset often espouse the notion of "tough love"—that the only way to help a person with SUD is to let them suffer (or hit "rock bottom"). In reality, when I have seen tough love in action, I see a lot of toughness, sometimes masking as abuse, but little love. There is a vast difference between enabling someone—like buying them drugs or making excuses for their behaviors—and helping them, which could include providing them transportation to treatment. Likewise, codependency, such as sacrificing someone's own well-being for the good of their partner, is not the same thing as trying to help.

Finally, the concept of *triangulation* is often present in family systems. The basic idea of triangulation is that two people in a system have a problem, but instead of dealing with it directly, they involve a third person. This third person may act as a scapegoat for their problems or as a go-between for them. For example, one parent has SUD, and the other parent is aware of it, but rather than talk about it, they focus their concern on their child. Another example could be parents who are separated or divorced and use a child to communicate with each other. Involving the other person reduces tension between the two people, but does not solve the initial problem (CSAT, 2015).

Helping vs. Enabling

When it comes to substance use, people sometimes confuse helping with enabling. Although both helping and enabling involve doing things for other people, there is an important difference between the two. When we *help* someone, we do things for other people who cannot do so for themselves. With enabling, we do things for people who can and should do those things for themselves. When enabling occurs within the context of addictive behavior, it allows the substance use to continue.

Things people cannot do for themselves

Doing things for other people

Things people can and should do for themselves

How Do Others Help (or Enable) You?

Recognizing everything that others do for you is an important part of your recovery journey, as is differentiating between helping and enabling. Use the following questions to determine how other people are currently helping (and possibly enabling) you.

How can you tell the difference between helping and enabling?

Who has enabled you (or is enabling you now)?

How did they (or are they) enabling you?

How did you come to realize that you were being enabled?

What would you like to change?

Who are people in your life who can help you without enabling you?

How can these people help you (and not enable you)?

How can you ask them for help?

How Do You Enable Others?

As you examine your SUD, it is not uncommon to realize that you may be enabling others. You could be enabling them with regard to their own substance use problems or with something completely unrelated. Use the following questions to explore if (and how) you might be enabling others.

How do you define enabling?

Who have you enabled (or are enabling now)?

How have you enabled others (or how might you be enabling others now)?

How did you come to realize that you were enabling them?

How could you be helpful to them without enabling them?

FAMILY ROLES AND RULES IMPACTED BY SUBSTANCE USE

Within the family structure, each member plays several roles, such as that of the parent, economic provider, strategic planner, child, and so on. In families with SUD, these roles emerge in response to the person with SUD and are a way to maintain homeostasis in the family, often to the detriment of individual members. For example, one member may assume the responsibilities of the person with SUD, thus freeing the other person to use substances. Another member may act out to distract people outside of the family from seeing SUD within the family system. Examples of these roles are included in the next handout.

All families maintain some sort of boundaries by separating themselves from those who are not in the family. Some boundaries are more flexible than others. These boundaries can create spoken or implied rules about the information that can or cannot be shared with others. For example, a family might want to keep a medical diagnosis private from the rest of their community until they are ready to share. Among families with SUD, one common rule is that no one is allowed to talk about the individual's substance use problems, especially to people outside the family. Doing so might shine a light on the person with SUD, which could impact their ability to continue using. Remember, at this point of treatment, the family's goal, no matter how unhealthy it may be, is to maintain homeostasis, even if that means continued use by the person with SUD. Understanding these roles and rules is crucial to engaging the family in treatment.

Roles in Families with SUD

The following is a list of roles that people may assume in a family with SUD, along with some characteristics for each type of role. Not every role is present in every family, and sometimes more than one person fills a role.

Identified addict (IA):

- The person who has SUD

- Often an adult and typically one of the monetary providers for the family

- Surrounds themselves with denial, which is perpetuated by the family system

- The IA may not be the only person in the family with SUD

Supportive enabler (SE):

- Usually an adult, often the spouse or partner of the person with SUD

- Does for the IA everything they can, including what the IA should be doing for themselves

- Protects the IA from the consequences of their SUD

- Also keeps other roles in line by encouraging them to maintain those roles

- May become so comfortable in their role that they will sabotage the IA's recovery work because they have ordered their life around the IA's use

Hostile enabler/resident expert:

- Typically an adult in the extended family, but can also be a stepparent

- Tells the SE what they are doing wrong regarding the IA

- In reality, they may not want the SE to stop enabling (and by extension, may not want the IA to get better) because this would rob them of their role

- Often passive-aggressive toward the IA

Hero:

- Usually the oldest child

- Assumes a lot of the SE's responsibilities by taking care of the IA

- Excels in school, sports, and other areas to get attention from the IA and the enablers

- Receives some positive attention from the family, but all of this is in vain, leading to a hollow feeling

Scapegoat:

- Functions as a mirror to the hero, providing a focus for the family's blame, shame, and negative energy

- Acts out to receive this negative attention

- Blamed for the IA's use

- Often develops SUD

Lost child:

- Goes out of their way to avoid getting any attention (negative or positive) from others

- Pathologically shy and avoidant

- Often cared for by the hero

Mascot:

- Attempts to deflect attention away from the family's problems and defuse tension with humor

- Helps the family convince themselves that they are "normal" or "okay"

- Acts in a superficial, often "cute," manner

- Is often spoiled and can lack empathy for others

Family Roles Then and Now

There are a variety of roles that can emerge in families, with each role serving a different purpose in the family system. Oftentimes, these roles develop to create the illusion that things are functioning well in the family, even if they are falling apart. Use the following questions to look at the roles in your family, paying special attention to see if any need to change.

What roles were present in your family when you were growing up?

What roles did you play? What roles did other people in your family play?

How did these roles protect one or more family member's drug use?

What were the penalties for stepping out of a role?

Look at your current family (this can include your biological family or your family of choice). What roles are in place? Who plays what roles?

What are three steps you can take to begin changing these roles?

Rules in Families Impacted by SUD

1. **Don't talk (or don't have problems):** This is one of the more common rules in families impacted by SUD. The idea here is that "If we don't talk about a problem, we don't have a problem" or "Substance use only becomes a problem when someone points it out or makes a big deal about it." This rule also extends to other problems that are not directly connected with SUD, because *any* family problem—such as poor school attendance, fighting, employment issues—may expose the person with SUD to outsiders.

2. **Don't trust:** Exposing a family member's SUD to people outside of the family can negatively impact the person with SUD and the entire family. To facilitate this, family members are often taught not to trust anyone. Trust is viewed as a sign of weakness and is discouraged at all costs.

3. **Don't feel:** When a family member vocalizes their feelings, it brings more pain to the family. It is therefore better to not have any feelings than to risk having to deal with painful emotions. Just as the person with SUD uses drugs or alcohol in order to feel numb, the goal is for the family to feel numb as well.

4. **Don't behave differently:** This rule is based on the family's desire for homeostasis—to maintain the status quo even when it is unhealthy. Behaving differently would cause chaos in the family system, and chaos threatens the family's homeostasis. This issue often emerges in couples work, particularly when one partner enters recovery. It is not unusual to hear the other partner say, "I liked it better when they were using. I'm used to that." We go with what we know or what we are used to. In many cases, the partner did not really want their loved one to resume use (although some did); they were merely remarking how different things were and how this took some getting used to.

5. **Don't blame SUD:** The goal is to blame anything—or anyone—else for the family's problems. The family may blame a child (i.e., the scapegoat), their life circumstances, politics, or their finances—anything other than SUD.

6. **Behave as the person with SUD wants:** The person with SUD often has a lot of power in the family, whether it is physical, financial, or emotional. As a result, their SUD usually supersedes all other aspects of the family. If people don't behave as the person with SUD wants, the drug use may not be able to continue, and the person with SUD may negatively exercise some of their power by becoming physically (or emotionally) violent, or they may leave the family.

7. **Do better and be responsible:** This rule applies to everyone except the person with SUD. The goal is to compensate for the substance user's actions. If everyone else looks good, the person with SUD may be given credit for this, or at least they can likely avoid having their SUD visible to others. However, family members know that despite their efforts and successes, they will never be good enough.

8. **Don't have fun:** Unless it involves substance use, and even then, don't have so much fun that you get into trouble. For many families in which there is a member with SUD, fun is defined by substance use. Therefore, only the person with SUD can have fun by getting intoxicated. Some family members may also be so busy keeping the family in balance that there is no room for fun.

Family Rules Then and Now

All families have rules (some spoken, some implied). Some rules are in place for safety reasons (e.g., don't cross the street without stopping to look for traffic), while other rules are in place to protect people in the family (e.g., a family member's substance use). Use the following questions to consider some of the protective rules in your family, including which rules might need to change.

What were the rules your family had when you were growing up, either spoken or implied?

How many of these rules were to protect one or more family member's drug use?

What were the penalties for breaking a rule?

Look at your current family (this can include your biological family or your family of choice). What rules are in place? Why are these rules in place?

Are there any rules in place to protect someone's drug use? This may include you.

What are three steps you can take to begin changing rules that protect a person's drug use?

TYPES OF FAMILY THERAPY

Although many different types of family therapy can be used in the treatment of SUD, in this next section, I will focus on three prominent approaches: structural-strategic family therapy (SSFT), Bowen family systems therapy (BFST), and community reinforcement and family training (CRAFT).

Methods of Family Therapy Commonly Used for SUD

Structural-strategic family therapy (SSFT)	• Used when one or more members of the family, referred to as a subsystem, has too much power over the other members. • One of the most important concepts of SSFT is to identify and replace unhealthy subsystems with balanced systems. • It is important for clinicians to get a good feel for how the family members communicate with one another and what the relationships are between each member. • It is also important to understand how each member regards boundaries—within and outside the family. • Key interventions include manipulating space, communication skills, role playing, problem tracking, and problem-solving.
Bowen family systems therapy (BFST)	• BFST views the family as a single emotional unit, with each member being emotionally interdependent from another. • This method sees patterns that persist across generations and are often passed down, making them unavoidable to certain members of the family. • One of the most important concepts of BFST is to encourage family members to break away from the enmeshment of family bonds. • Key interventions include analyzing a genogram, an ancestral diagram to visually take account of repetitive behaviors or hereditary patterns within a family. • Identifying and being aware of these patterns can help with creating boundaries and relationships, as well as showing that each member is their own distinct individual.

Community reinforcement and family training (CRAFT)	• CRAFT is designed to help people encourage loved ones with SUD, especially those balking at treatment options, to seek help.
	• One of the most important concepts of CRAFT is helping people understand their loved one's SUD, even if they do not ultimately decide to get treatment.
	• Key interventions include identifying consequences, preventing dangerous situations, problem-solving, and making plans.

STRUCTURAL-STRATEGIC FAMILY THERAPY

SSFT is a type of therapy that aims to help families recognize and change behavioral patterns of one or more members. SSFT assumes that the family system's power and structure is greater than the individual's power and that the family determines an individual's behaviors to an extent. Family roles and boundaries, as well as the places where power is vested in the family system, establish how a family system works. As part of this system, SSFT considers the role of subsystems, or "mini" systems, within the larger family structure. For example, parents can form a subsystem, as can siblings or spouses. These subsystems can become problematic when they work to hoard power or create boundaries that protect unhealthy behaviors. In the case of SUD, the clinician will help the family recognize behaviors within subsystems that support substance use, aiming to replace these with more balanced systems.

In addition, the question of executive authority—that is, who holds the power in the family—forms a central role in SSFT. In most families, adults hold this authority, allowing them to determine how the family functions and how to maintain order in the family. However, in families with SUD, the power is often held by the person with SUD or the supportive enabler. In a family where these specific roles decide the function and order, priorities and rules can be immensely different compared to households without substance use.

In some cases, the adults *think* they have executive authority when the power actually lies with another member. I once worked with a blended family system of eight people in which the third-oldest child, who was 18, ran the family. Nearly every decision the family made was done in an attempt to avoid triggering the 18-year-old, who would invariably respond with verbal and physical abuse. Through our work together, I helped the adults see how they had ceded power to their child, and we worked to set appropriate boundaries, including consequences for inappropriate or abusive behaviors. With time, the adults were able to reassert their authority and regain functioning over the family system.

Like other forms of family therapy, SSFT also considers how people in the family differentiate themselves from each other (including parents from their children), how the family interacts within the larger environment, and how the family's boundaries (or lack thereof) protect the people in the family who use substances.

Communication is an important concept of practice as well—clinicians should get a good feel for how the family members communicate with one another. Are they aggressive, passive-aggressive, or assertive with one another? Or is there a major lack of communication in the family? How do people advocate for their needs within the family system? Role playing can be an effective way for clinicians to demonstrate effective communication skills and allow the opportunity for families to practice their new skills.

In order to change substance use behaviors within the family, SSFT identifies the role that SUD plays in the family while the clinician guides change in the family structure. Key interventions include manipulating space, communication skills, role playing, problem tracking, and problem-solving, which are each described in the following handouts and worksheets.

Manipulating Space

Manipulating space is an effective technique when you have gotten to know a family and understand the roles people play and where power is distributed. The intervention is simple: Ask family members to change where they are sitting or who they are sitting near in session. Often, making this request to change positions will generate a reaction from one or more members, revealing underlying tension, hidden alliances, and power dynamics—which means you can start doing some real therapeutic work.

Consider the following case example.

Mr. and Mrs. Brown—and their adolescent children, Leia and Luke—have been attending family therapy sessions for three weeks. This is their fourth session. The Browns have been ordered to participate in family therapy as a condition of Leia's probation. She has a history of petty larceny and cannabis possession. Previous sessions have yielded little in terms of content because the family is resentful that they are all required to participate in treatment (which is not unusual in court-ordered counseling).

Mrs. Brown drinks heavily, but she denies having a problem with alcohol, and Mr. Brown is generally a passive participant in family matters. Leia tries to actively separate herself from the family, while her younger brother, Luke, protects his mother and deflects tension from her. As a result, Mrs. Brown often keeps Luke close to her. The clinician's goal in the fourth session is to use the manipulating space technique to bring some of these systems to the attention of the family.

Clinician:	Good to see everyone today. I've noticed that you all sit in the same spot each session, so today I'm asking you to move.
Mrs. Brown:	[*Tension in her voice*] Why?
Clinician:	Fair question. Sometimes it helps to see a situation from a different perspective, and this can help. Luke, I'd like you to move to that chair, away from your mother on the coach. Leia, could you move to the couch next to your mom? Mr. Brown, if you could sit next to your wife on the other side, that would be great.
Luke:	It's weird not sitting next to my mom.
Clinician:	Why's that?
Luke:	Because I always sit there.

Leia:	Who cares? I don't want to sit here.
Clinician:	Why's that?
Leia:	I'd rather be by myself.
Mrs. Brown:	Well, that's typical—you don't like to spend time with the family.
Leia:	Yeah, you're right.
Clinician:	Why don't you want to spend time with your family?
Leia:	Drama, lots of drama.
Luke:	Which you cause…
Leia:	Do I?!
Clinician:	Hold on a second. Mr. Brown, all of this is happening, and you appear to be lost.
Mrs. Brown:	Yes, Charles, be a parent for Christ's sake!
Mr. Brown:	Um…what do you want me to say?
Clinician:	Well, what do you think about what your children are saying?
Mr. Brown:	I think it is wrong, but I don't know what to do.
Mrs. Brown:	Hmmm…
Clinician:	What does that mean?
Mr. Brown:	[*Less passive*] It means I don't know what to say. I feel like you don't care what I have to say anyway.
Mrs. Brown:	Me?
Mr. Brown:	Yes, you! All I hear is yelling. You yelling at Leia, Leia yelling at you, Luke yelling at Leia, you drinking…
Mrs. Brown:	What does that have to do with anything?
Luke:	Yeah, Mom just…
Clinician:	Hold on, Luke. You just interrupted your parents when they were talking.
Luke:	So?
Clinician:	They are the adults. [*Luke glares at the clinician*]
Mrs. Brown:	So what if I drink?
Leia:	I smoke weed and you guys lose your shit over that…
Clinician:	That is an issue, Leia, and something we need to discuss, but I think your folks want to at least talk about the drinking right now.

Notice how simply asking people to move to different locations in the room created tension and conversation. The clinician wanted to move Mr. Brown into a more active role, while at the same time pushing Leia to engage with the family and decreasing the alliance between Luke and his mother. In doing so, Mrs. Brown's alcohol use came up again and appeared to be a big reason why Mr. Brown had checked out on his family and become passive. Bringing Mrs. Brown's alcohol use in the open by manipulating space created opportunities to examine how everyone's substance use was impacting the family—and that's where the real work begins.

Communication Skills

How we speak with each other, and how we listen to one another, has a huge impact on how we treat each other. Use the following questions to help you examine the communication styles in your family and provide a new way to communicate.

How did your parents communicate with you and your siblings in your family of origin?

How did you communicate with your parents and siblings in your family of origin?

What was helpful to you in terms of how others communicated with you? What was not helpful?

How would you describe the communication within your current family? (This can include your biological family or your family of choice)

How would you like to see your current family's communication change?

Using "I" Statements

"I" statements are an effective way to communicate your thoughts and needs in a way that other people are more likely to accept. In contrast to "you" statements—which can feel accusatory and cause the other person to become defensive—"I" statements are how *you* are feeling or thinking, as opposed to the other person. This makes it more likely that the other person will listen to you and not get defensive. It is also important to remain aware of your voice tone, which can often convey more about what you're trying to say than the actual words you use. Here's a simple "I" statement formula:

> "I feel _____ when you _____ because _____."

For example:

"You" statement: Why the hell don't you stop drinking?!

"I" statement: I feel worried when you drink because I am concerned about your health.

In the example of the "I" statement, notice how the person expressed their feelings but did so in a non-accusatory (and likely less angry sounding) way.

For practice, try reframing the following "you" statements into "I" statements. Some examples of feelings have been included in the word bank below, or you can come up with your own.

annoyed	enraged	uneasy	worthless	hesitant
outraged	desperate	offended	disappointed	dejected
sad	confused	upset	heartbroken	powerless
agitated	worried	furious	embarrassed	manipulated
frightened	nervous	uncertain	depressed	frustrated
anxious	alone	inferior	panicked	miserable

1. You told me you were going to cut back on your use, but that doesn't seem to be the case.

   I feel _____ when you _____

   because _____.

2. Why can't you be on time? You're always late!

   I feel _____ when you _____

   because _____.

3. You're so lazy—you never clean up after yourself!

   I feel _____ when you _____

   because _____.

4. You can't ever seem to follow through on your word. No one can depend on you.

   I feel _____ when you _____

   because _____.

Family Role Playing

Role playing can help families practice new social skills and develop an understanding of other family members' perspectives. Prior to introducing role playing into the session, it is important 1) for the family to have some motivation for self-examination and 2) for the environment to be safe for people to be open. Unless and until these two factors are present, use role playing only for skill building and not for interpersonal work, such as role playing how another family member acts.

Raquel and her mother, Ms. Garcia, have been attending family sessions to learn how to express themselves without yelling and how to handle conflict the next time it occurs. Although they made some progress when "I" statements were introduced, it has been a difficult process overall. There is clearly a lot of anger between the two of them, but it is hidden under the surface. To identify the source of this anger, the clinician attempts something different by asking Raquel and her mother to switch roles with each other.

Clinician:	Raquel, you've mentioned that you get scared when your mother starts yelling.
Raquel:	Yeah.
Ms. Garcia:	I think you're embellishing again.
Clinician:	Let's see how it might look. Raquel, you mentioned that your mom got angry when you came home past curfew last week. Why don't you try switching roles and be your mom in this scenario?
Raquel:	Awesome!
Clinician:	…and Ms. Garcia, you be Raquel.
Ms. Garcia:	Okay.
Clinician:	Remember that the goal here is not to insult each other, it is to be as accurate as possible in terms of what you see and hear when the other person communicates with you. Now who wants to start?
Raquel:	I will. [*Takes a minute to get into "character." As she starts talking, she begins to slur her words.*] Where the hell have you been?!
Ms. Garcia:	[*Speaking in a demonstratively higher voice*] Why do you care! I can do what I want!
Raquel:	[*Still slurring her words*] 'Cause I'm your mom, dammit!

Clinician:	Hold on a minute. Raquel, why are you slurring your words like that?
Raquel:	[*Using her own voice again*] Because that's how she talks.
Clinician:	I don't hear your mom slurring her words here.
Raquel:	But she does that a lot at home, especially in the afternoon and at night.
Ms. Garcia:	[*Using her own voice again*] You mean when I take my meds?
Raquel:	Yeah.
Ms. Garcia:	Those are prescription medications for my anxiety.
Raquel:	But you take a lot of them, more than you used to, sometimes with liquor. And sometimes you say weird stuff and don't even remember what you said the next day.
Ms. Garcia:	You are changing the subject. What's this got to do with you staying out too late?
Raquel:	Because I hate being around you when you're like that!
Clinician:	It seems like we're getting to something important we need to discuss.

The circumstances revealed during the activity can now be addressed in family therapy (and likely individual therapy for Ms. Garcia to address her benzodiazepine and alcohol use).

Problem Tracking

Problems usually do not occur in isolation but instead manifest through a series of events. With problem tracking, clinicians help family members increase their awareness of the series of events and interactions that contributed to the presenting problem. Helping clients identify problems, how they start, and what they lead to is a key component of family treatment. To use problem tracking, the clinician chooses a point in time in the past that is related to the presenting issue (usually by asking the client or a family member, "When did you notice _____?"). Then the clinician works with the family to slowly move backward from that point to the present, intentionally and methodically identifying interactions, behaviors, and events that led to the current problem.

Consider the following case example:

The Rollins family has been attending family therapy for three weeks. The family consists of Mr. Rollins and Mrs. Rollins (who have been married for three years), and Mr. Rollins's three children from a previous marriage: Alex, Ben, and Cooper. Mr. Rollins says that he and his ex-wife have an amicable relationship and that they co-parent well. They live near each other and split custody of their children every other week.

Although the children adjusted well to Mrs. Rollins as their new stepmother during the first two years of their marriage, for the past year, Alex and Ben have become increasingly defiant by talking back, breaking curfew, getting poor grades, and (as was recently discovered) using alcohol and marijuana. Mr. and Mrs. Rollins are most concerned about the substance use.

Clinician:	I want to try something today called problem tracking. It's a way to dig down into problems and see everything that is going on.
Mrs. Rollins:	I thought the problem was the alcohol and pot use.
Clinician:	That's certainly part of the problem, but what else is involved?
Mr. Rollins:	Isn't this just a way to avoid dealing with the drug problem?
Clinician:	What is it that you're worried about?
Mr. Rollins:	That they will continue to use, and it will develop into a big problem. It seems like this is just a way to find something to blame for the drug use.
Clinician:	I hear what you are saying, Mr. Rollins. My goal is not to find blame or excuses for the drug use. As we talked about in previous sessions, one family member's actions impact the rest of the family and vice versa. Let's give this a shot. Would you all like to focus on the drug use?

All:	[*Nods*]
Clinician:	When did you find out about the drug use?
Mrs. Rollins:	About four months ago, I guess.
Clinician:	And how did you notice?
Mr. Rollins:	First it was the grades. The kids have always been excellent students, but first Alex, then Ben, started bringing home Ds and Fs.
Clinician:	Alex and Ben, what do you think?
Alex:	About our grades?
Clinician:	Yes, do you think there is a connection between the drug use and your grades dropping?
Alex:	I'm not gonna tell you when I started smoking…
Clinician:	And I didn't say you had to…
Ben:	I think for me it did.
Clinician:	Did what?
Ben:	When I started smoking, and drinking too I guess, I stopped doing my homework.
Clinician:	So just to backtrack, your parents noticed the grades dropping, and then they found out about the pot and the alcohol, but are you saying that the drug use came before the grades dropped?
Alex:	I'm not saying anything…
Clinician:	And I can't make you, but anything you can add might be helpful. [*Alex doesn't say anything.*]
Ben:	I think it happened that way.
Mr. Rollins:	Why did you start?
Ben:	[*Looks quickly at Alex, then turns away from her*]. I guess I just wanted to.
Mr. Rollins:	No, there's always a reason…
Clinician:	Not always.
Mrs. Rollins:	Were you not happy?
Alex:	That's rich!
Mr. Rollins:	What does that mean?
Ben:	What do you care?

Clinician:	So there was something before this? [*Silence*]. Cooper, you are awfully quiet. Are you okay? [*Cooper starts to cry.*]
Cooper:	[*Sobs*] No. I just want to go back home.
Alex:	[*Mutters*] Whatever that is.
Clinician:	What do you mean by that?
Ben:	I feel like we don't have a home.

Further work with the family revealed that things were not as smooth as Mr. and Mrs. Rollins had painted them to be in the beginning. Despite the claim that Mr. Rollins and his ex-wife got along amicably, he did not share that they did not communicate clearly and often talked negatively about each other in front of their children. The children had also developed a growing resentment about having to switch houses every other week and were later able to discuss feeling powerless over this. More importantly, their parents' divorce had hurt them deeply. This entire process pushed the parents to re-evaluate their communication styles and to give their children greater input on how they would schedule custody time, especially as their children got older.

The issue of substance use was not forgotten in all of this. There were consequences for Alex and Ben's actions, and limitations on what they could do until they regained the adults' trust and demonstrated healthier choices, but in this case/family, the substance use presented as secondary to addressing the emotional climate/health of the family.

Problem-Solving

Problems usually have more than one solution, and it's sometimes necessary to try several times before you can effectively solve a problem. Use this worksheet to examine a problem you are currently dealing with as a family. First, identify a problem that you'd like to work on in more depth. Then come up with four possible solutions to this problem and identify the pros and cons of each solution. As a family, use the advantages and disadvantages of each solution to rank them in order of preference or eliminate them one by one until only one remains. Finally, pick a solution and evaluate the results of your choice. By working together as a family on this problem, it can help bring you closer together.

Problem: _____

_____

Solution #1: _____

Pros	Cons

Solution #2: _____

Pros	Cons

Solution #3: _____

Pros	Cons

Solution #4: _____

Pros	Cons

Rank each solution in order of preference:

1. _____

2. _____

3. _____

4. _____

Once you have chosen a solution, implement it at home. Evaluate the outcome after some time has passed to see if it has solved the problem at hand. If the problem persists, you can try the same exercise with new solutions.

BOWEN FAMILY SYSTEMS THERAPY

BFST holds that all family dysfunction, including substance use, comes from ineffective management of anxiety in the family system (Bacon, 2019; CSAT, 2015). Anxiety, in this model, creates family dysfunction. Given that BFST views the family as emotionally interdependent, this approach attempts to reduce anxiety in the family by encouraging people to become more differentiated, more autonomous, and less enmeshed in the family's emotional system.

When it comes to SUD, the theory maintains that a person uses alcohol or drugs to temporarily reduce anxiety, and when the entire family can justifiably focus on the individual who uses drugs as the problem, it deflects attention from other sources of anxiety. Because BFST sees the family as a single emotional unit, only one person needs to maintain a calm, non-anxious, meaningful presence to change the entire system. As a result, BFST often works through one member who is motivated to make changes; this is often a person who is not using substances.

One of the techniques that BFST uses is the genogram, which can help families visualize patterns of behavior across generations and provide an understanding of problems that currently impact the family. The genogram is a tool rather than a treatment intervention in that it creates a "map" of the family system that can highlight where substance use behaviors or other challenges (i.e., sources of anxiety) impact the family. It can also be used to identify triangles and other alliances in the family system. Even as clinicians examine the system via this map, it is important to emphasize to clients that while they are part of a family system (and are shaped by this system), they are also distinct and independent individuals within their families.

To illustrate how the genogram works, I've provided a sample one here using Denny from chapter 1, whom you recall had several relatives with SUD. For this exercise, let's assume Denny is 18 and still living at home, and he and his family are in the session together. As a group, we complete the genogram, which covers four generations. Both of Denny's parents note that their fathers had alcohol use disorder and died relatively young as a result. Growing up in homes with an active alcoholic, Denny's parents explain to him that they avoided drinking as much as possible. Denny's father points out that his older brother (and only sibling) also has SUD. Denny's mother explains that she started working in a hospital-based substance use treatment program years ago because of her experiences growing up in a home with a parent who drank.

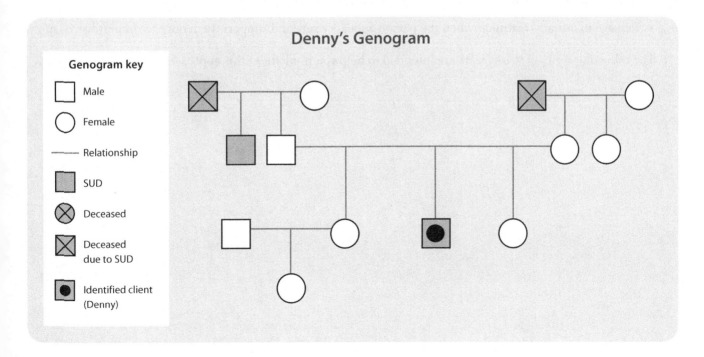

Denny's Genogram

As you can see, Denny's older and younger sister have not developed SUD, and at this time, Denny is ambivalent about whether he has a problem with substances or not. Denny's parents share their concerns about Denny's actions, noting the family history of SUD. This will hopefully lead to conversations between Denny and his parents and possible strategies to address his substance use.

COMMUNITY REINFORCEMENT AND FAMILY TRAINING

CRAFT is an intervention designed to help family members encourage their unmotivated or treatment-refusing loved ones to seek help for their SUD. The initial focus of CRAFT is to help these family members understand their loved one's SUD and ways that they can help them. Even if the person with SUD chooses not to engage in treatment, the changes within the family system will benefit all members of the family.

Rather than working with the person with SUD to accomplish this goal, CRAFT works directly with the family members involved. CRAFT recognizes that people with SUD may be unaware of their drug problem and its impact on the family, or they may be ambivalent about making changes, particularly about entering treatment. Therefore, it uses many of the assumptions and practices of MI, particularly in terms of taking a non-confrontational approach. The following are some of the components of the CRAFT approach that loved ones will learn to do (Meyers et al., 1998):

- Raise awareness of the negative consequences caused by the family member's drug use and highlight the benefits of treatment.

- Learn specific strategies to prevent dangerous situations, like the person with SUD driving or being placed in a childcare capacity.

- Use contingency management to reinforce non-using behaviors and to change drug use.

- Practice social skills training to improve relationship communication and critical thinking skills.

- Plan activities that interfere and compete with the person's drug use.

- Practice strategies to interfere with actual and potential drug use.

- Prepare to initiate treatment when the person appears ready and support them once treatment has begun.

The following series of worksheets are intended to help you implement this approach with family members.

Consequences of Your Loved One's SUD

Sometimes family members are the first people to realize that a person has a problem with substances. Use the following questions to discuss your loved one's substance use and how it has affected your family.

Which family member do you think has a substance use problem?

When did you first realize this?

What have you tried to do?

Which of these worked? Which didn't?

What do you think will happen if nothing changes?

What changes would you like to see?

What are things you could do as a family that will interfere with your loved one's use?

Who else can you involve with this plan?

Where do you hope things will be in six months? A year?

Prevent Dangerous Situations

People change when they are ready, not when we want them to change. Until that time, it is important to develop a plan to keep your loved one safe and to prevent potentially dangerous situations that might occur as a result of SUD. Use the following questions to consider how you can prevent these situations.

Secure any weapons in the home. What do you need to secure? Who will be responsible for securing these weapons?

Secure medications, including over-the-counter products. What do you need to secure? Who is responsible for securing these medications?

People with SUD may deplete their family's finances, especially if they are in charge of the family's money. Who is monitoring the family finances?

People with opioid use disorder should have access to naloxone (Narcan) at all times. It should be available regardless of the substances that people are using, as fentanyl is often found in non-opioid substances. Is naloxone available? Who is trained in administering it?

When someone drives a car under the influence of substances, it creates a significant safety hazard. How will you keep your loved one from driving while intoxicated?

Family Problem-Solving Activity

If your loved one is ambivalent about making a change (or refusing to make a change) to their substance use, it can be hard to help them get treatment. However, one way to indirectly address their SUD is to plan activities that interfere and compete with their drug use. In this worksheet, you'll use the prompts provided to identify the specific problem related to their substance use, brainstorm possible solutions (and obstacles to each solution) and make a plan. An example is provided for you first, provided by a template for you to write in your own answers.

1. Define the problem as specifically as possible
Isaiah uses alcohol and cocaine starting when he comes home on Friday after work and throughout Saturday.

2. Brainstorm possible solutions
Schedule family activities throughout Friday afternoon and Saturday
Invite people over who Isaiah will be less likely to use around
Do not keep any alcohol in the house
Ignore Isaiah
Call the police when Isaiah leaves to purchase cocaine
Ask Isaiah to leave the home

3. Eliminate less attractive solutions (cross them out)

Schedule family activities throughout Friday afternoon and Saturday

Invite people over who Isaiah will be less likely to use around

~~Do not keep any alcohol in the house~~

~~Ignore Isaiah~~

~~Call the police when Isaiah leaves to purchase cocaine~~

~~Ask Isaiah to leave the home~~

4. Select a potential solution

Schedule family activities throughout Friday afternoon and Saturday.

5. Generate potential obstacles and address each obstacle

Problem: Isaiah may not want to go.

Solution: Incorporate the kids' sporting activities into our plans, as Isaiah never wants to miss a game.

Problem: This could get costly.

Solution: Search online for free or low-cost activities in the area that do not have alcohol available.

6. Make a plan

Picnic at Maymont Park on Friday after work. Page's soccer game on Saturday morning. Robbie's baseball game Saturday afternoon. Food festival in the afternoon. Family night hike.

7. Evaluate outcomes at the next session

1. Define the problem as specifically as possible

2. Brainstorm possible solutions

3. Eliminate less attractive solutions (cross them out)
4. Select a potential solution

5. Generate potential obstacles and address each obstacle

6. Make a plan

7. Evaluate outcomes at the next session

Change Plan

People change when they are ready, not when we want them to change. Therefore, you need to be prepared to meet your loved one with a plan when and if they decide they are ready to change.* Use the following questions to help you develop a change plan for when your loved one is ready to address their substance use.

How will we know when _____ is ready to make changes?

What resources can we have on standby when they are ready?

Medical needs. What medical provider(s) might we need to refer them to?

Treatment needs. What are our options for SUD assessment and treatment placement? How will we handle things if they change their mind about treatment?

_____

* Making changes can cause people to experience feelings of hopelessness, especially at first. Sometimes, they may see suicide as a viable option for their problems. If your loved one talks about harming themselves at any point during the change process, get them to the nearest emergency department for a thorough assessment.

Relationship needs. This situation impacts all of us. What do other people in the family need in terms of emotional support?

Housing. What if they need to live elsewhere while they stabilize? How will we pay for this?

Other support. What other resources may they need?

Who else should be involved in this process?

How do we support each other in this process?

10

Group Therapy Strategies

Group counseling has been used to treat SUD for many years (White, 2014). Oftentimes, the group format helps clients feel less alone in their struggles and provides them a means by which to receive encouragement, feedback, and modeling from their peers. This peer interaction can serve an important foundation for their recovery and, in many ways, can be superior to individual treatment because:

- Peers carry credibility.

- Positive peer pressure can be helpful.

- The therapist's role is spread among group members.

- More people can be treated simultaneously when compared with individual therapy.

- The group culture and support can extend outside of the group meeting.

- Group meetings provide a safe environment where clients can practice new social and critical thinking skills with one another.

Groups can be open or closed and time-limited or ongoing. Open groups are generally open to a variety of people, whereas closed groups are set up for specific client needs. Time-limited groups begin and end with a specified timeframe. Open groups have members enter and exit the group as long as the group remains in existence.

TYPES OF GROUP THERAPY

There are many types of group therapy, including psychoeducational groups, skills development groups, problem-solving groups, support groups, and process groups. The following table provides more information on each type.

Psychoeducational groups	• Provide information to clients (or their families) about their substance use and its consequences • Usually a time-limited, open group format involving many people (sometimes as many as 30+) • Is typically highly structured and follows a manual • Often used with clients at the start of treatment who are in the pre-contemplative or contemplative stage

Skills development groups	• Helps clients develop the skills needed to achieve and maintain recovery, including skills unrelated to SUD (e.g., budgeting, nutrition planning) • Involves a time-limited group format (either open or closed) that is smaller in size (typically 6–8 clients)
Problem-solving groups	• Views SUD as a learned behavior that can be modified through behavioral reinforcement, contingency management strategies, and response desensitization • Includes a time-limited group format (either open or closed) with 10–12 members • May follow a treatment manual or use educational materials • Goals are set by each member and the focus of the group is on immediate problems
Support groups	• Allows peers to role model healthy behaviors and use their personal experiences to help each other and even people outside of the group • Typically involves an ongoing group format (open or closed), with varying group sizes (3–30+ people) • Have been a part of SUD treatment longer than any other type of group • Are usually less-directive than other groups
Process groups	• Focus is on uncovering underlying patterns that contribute to substance use or interfere with recovery • Can involve an ongoing or time-limited format (open or closed) that is usually smaller in size (fewer than 10 members) • Leaders track the functioning of individual group members and the group as a whole • Should only be led by trained clinicians who understand group process and group roles

Topics for Psychoeducational Groups

12-step peer groups	Intoxication and withdrawal symptoms
Assertiveness training skills	Levels of substance use
Communication skills	Mental health and SUD
Developing a safety plan	Parenting a child with SUD
Domestic partner violence	Physical health and SUD
Expressing gratitude	Talking with others about SUD
Forgiving others	Recovery and relationships
Forgiving ourselves	SMART Recovery and other support groups
Handling our feelings	Spirituality
Harm reduction	Trauma basics
Having a parent with SUD	Types of SUD treatment
Helping others	Understanding a loved one's SUD
How can we allow others to help us?	What is recovery?
How does SUD impact families?	

Topics for Skill Development Groups

Interpersonal/Relational

Avoiding dangerous situations	Expressing your opinion
Being a good partner	Parenting basics
Being assertive without being a jerk	Self-disclosure
Building your support system	Setting boundaries
Creating safety plans	Starting a conversation

Practical

Budgeting	Job searching
Communicating with health care providers	Nutrition planning
Expressing your spirituality	Prepping for a job interview
Finding housing	Smart shopping
Finding recreational opportunities	

Preparing for Problem-Solving Groups

Our group's purpose is to work together to solve problems. We will start by identifying some of our shared challenges. Fill this form out on your own before starting the group so your group facilitators can identify common problems you can work on together.

Name five problems you would be willing to address in group. Rank them in order of importance.

1.

2.

3.

4.

5.

For each problem, what have you done so far to try to address it?

1.

2.

3.

4.

5.

How do you think group members can help each other with their problems?

Discussion Starters for Process Groups

1. Read a quote (does not have to be related to SUD or "inspirational" in nature) and have group members reflect on it or describe what it means to them.

2. "How are things with you today?"

3. "How were things yesterday? Over the weekend?"

4. "Does anyone have anything they want to share?"

5. "What do people think about what _____ shared?"

6. "How do you feel today?" (You may need to provide a list of feelings to get beyond happy, mad, sad, etc.)

7. On or around Thanksgiving or other holidays: "What are you thankful for?"

8. After or around January 1: "A lot of people make resolutions for the new year. What are some of yours?"

9. On or around Mother's Day or Father's Day: "This holiday brings up a lot of varied emotions. What are some things you're feeling now?" "What are some struggles you've had this week?"

10. For groups that have been working together: "What is something positive you can say to someone else in the group?" (Make sure everyone is included.)

11. "What is something we can celebrate today?"

12. "How have you managed cravings this week?"

13. "How did you manage negative feelings this past week?"

14. "What are you looking forward to (e.g., over the weekend, holiday)?"

GROUP FACILITATION

As a group facilitator, your overall role is to manage the environment without controlling the group. This involves role modeling respect and appropriate communication, clarifying communication through the use of "I" statements, and providing honest praise and validation. In addition, there will inevitably be differences between group members, so part of your role involves mediating these differences and learning how to address them with respect, as well as identifying commonalities between group members to help build cohesion.

In addition, it is important to confront inappropriate behaviors if group members do not confront them first, which often involves handling intoxicated group members. Be prepared for this possibility and don't take it personally. If someone is intoxicated in the meeting itself, they can be asked to leave (although be sure they can get home safely) and have them meet with you before coming to the next group meeting. As always, you can treat lapses like these as learning opportunities. As the intoxicated member may create urges to use among the rest of the group, take the opportunity to discuss the situation with the other members, touching on concepts like triggers, dangerous situations, and relapse.

The following pages provide you with additional information to set up group expectations, navigate different group roles, use icebreakers, and more.

Suggested Group Expectations

I recommend having only a few rules to facilitate your group. Instead of posting these expectations in the group space, have experienced group members explain the expectations each time a new member joins the group. Doing so helps reinforce the expected values among group members.

1. **Group starts and ends on time.** Members will not be admitted if they are more than _____ minutes late. I allow no more than 10 minutes, but I also tell clients that if they know they are going to be late, they should call before the start of group, in which case we'll let them in. If this develops into a pattern, we will discuss it.

2. **No eating in group.** Members are welcome to bring non-alcoholic beverages to group. I sometimes allow candy, but no food is allowed beyond this.

3. **Stay awake in group.**

4. **Confidentiality reigns supreme.** If people do not feel safe to speak up in group, then the group cannot work. What is said during the group *must* remain in group, with exceptions to situations that require mandated reporting (e.g., statements about abuse, neglect, or intent to harm oneself or others).

5. **Allow others to speak.** Everyone is entitled to their opinion.

6. **There is no such thing as a "dumb question."** Part of learning is being able to ask questions without being made to feel stupid.

Group Member Roles

The following is a list of roles that people may assume in a group, along with some strategies to manage each type of role. Not every role is present in every group, and sometimes more than one person fills a role. Members can also switch roles as groups evolve (Yalom, 1995).

Monopolist:

- Tries to use all the group's time and wants to remain the focus of the group

- **Strategy:** The group leader should "spread around" the focus of the group by directly calling on others throughout the meeting (members can be encouraged to speak but should not be forced).

Help-rejecting complainer:

- Will find a way to undermine any suggestion or help, no matter what someone else says

- **Strategy:** Don't get caught up in this power struggle. Instead, use MI skills to demonstrate to other group members how to address this behavior and bring them into the conversation. For instance, the clinician may say, "I keep hearing you say 'that won't work.' Could we ask other group members what they think? Maybe they have some ideas."

Silent member:

- Sits by passively and rarely participates in discussion

- **Strategy:** Do not force people to talk because sitting in a group is anxiety-provoking for many people. You may encourage people to speak up, but if they are attentive to what is happening in the group, they are still a part of the process.

Helicopter:

- Does not like to see others feel uncomfortable and will try to decrease their discomfort by "rescuing" them or by confronting any other members causing this discomfort

- **Strategy:** Gently point out to the person what they are doing, as many of them don't realize they're "rescuing" others, as they may fulfill a similar role in their family.

Clown:

- Does not like feeling uncomfortable and uses humor to defuse tension, often to the detriment of the group

- **Strategy:** Use the same approach as the Helicopter by pointing out to them what they are doing. If this does not decrease the Clown's actions, directly ask them to stop.

Bully:

- Uses fear and intimidation toward their peers to try to control the group

- **Strategy:** Groups in the more established stages will usually take on a bully with facilitator assistance, but in earlier stages, the facilitator may need to do this. Facilitators should set limits and consider removing bullies from the group should their behaviors make others feel unsafe.

Co-opter/therapist:

- Tries to undermine the therapist due to their desire to control others or avoid receiving criticism from the group or therapist

- **Strategy:** Do not take this personally, as part of the co-opter's strategy is to get you to react emotionally. Validate any statements they make that are accurate and set limits on things that are not valid.

Professional patient:

- Is committed to their role as a patient and has structured their self-concept around this; often displays a "been there, done that" or "I've tried everything, and nothing seems to work" attitude

- **Strategy:** Do not take this personally and accept that these clients can be emotionally draining. Use an MI approach of looking at exceptions and questioning all-or-nothing thinking.

Group Icebreakers

These activities are meant to help with group formation when the group is 15 people or fewer. Everyone needs to participate in the group (including you!). Keep it fun!

1. **Two truths and a lie.** Each person says three things about themselves, with two statements being true and the other being a lie. The other group members then guess which statement is a lie.

2. **People bingo.** Instead of containing numbers or letters, each bingo card is filled with different characteristics or life facts that may describe group members. There are templates available online.

3. **Line up in birth order.** Ask people to line up chronologically based on their birthday (e.g., November 2 comes after January 22). Variations can include not allowing people to talk or allowing only certain people to speak. You can also use another theme to line up group members.

4. **Rock-paper-scissors tournament.**

5. **Draw your family coat-of-arms.** Ask group members to draw the things that represent them and share with the group.

6. **"Have you ever…"** People stand up if they "have ever" done what the facilitator says. Keep this light-hearted; this is not the time for people to disclose serious things.

7. **Floating stick.** Get a broom handle and have each member support the stick using just one finger. See how group members are able to communicate with one another and work together to raise the stick to eye level (or over their heads) without dropping it.

8. **Name ball.** Toss a tennis ball to one person in the group, who will say their name and then toss it to someone else. This should continue until everyone has been "served" with the ball, after which the ball returns to the first person. See who can remember everyone's name. Next, see how quickly the group can toss the ball so that everyone touches it in the same order as the first time they were served.

9. **Group juggle.** Start like name ball, with one person throwing the ball until everyone has caught and thrown it, and the ball is back to the person who started. In this game, say the name of the person you are throwing the ball to. Once the group is in a rhythm, add more balls to the cycle. (My wife used to throw in a rubber chicken just for fun when we co-facilitated these activities years ago.)

10. **Group knot.** After the group forms a circle, ask each member to hold one hand of two other members, crossing arms and hands until the group is a human knot. Then see if the group can untangle itself without anyone letting go of the hands they are holding. (Only use this with people who are comfortable holding hands and being touched.)

After trying any of these activities, pose some questions to the group for them to process:

- How did the group change during the activity?

- How did the group communicate?

- How did the group solve problems?

- How were people included (or not included)?

- How did leadership develop?

- What might you do differently next time?

PROCESS OF GROUP FORMATION

Group formation typically follows a sequence of five stages, which begins when the group is first coming together and ends when the group terminates (Tucker, 1965, 1977 as cited in Boyle et al., 2009):

1. **Forming:** Group members learn about each other and look to the facilitator for guidance, safety, and orientation. The group facilitator is most active at this stage in leading the group, but some facilitators never allow the group to move beyond this level because they exert too much control over the group. If you're one of these facilitators, do your best to allow the group to evolve to the next stage. This will mean relinquishing some control and tolerating the resulting chaos— (e.g., storming). While this may be uncomfortable, it is necessary for the growth of the group.

2. **Storming:** This is the most challenging part of group work when group members compete for power (e.g., challenging the facilitator, talking over each other). Here, the facilitator must focus on problem-solving and looking for exceptions, especially when members work together. Groups are messy and take time to form. Stick with it.

3. **Norming:** This stage of group work emerges slowly—happening in fits and starts—from storming. Here, the focus is on cohesion, community building, problem-solving, and shared leadership. Facilitators should focus on maintaining a safe environment and should give power to the group.

4. **Performing:** At this stage, true interdependence is formed among group members. Group leaders do little at this point beyond taking on the role of observer and coach. Not all groups reach this stage.

5. **Adjourning:** In the final stage, the group comes to an end and members prepare to disengage from the relationships they have formed. Given that many clients have not had positive endings to relationships, it is important that the facilitator resumes a leadership position at this stage in order to provide meaningful closure for group members.

COMMON ERRORS MADE IN GROUP TREATMENT

Whether you are a beginning counselor or a more seasoned clinician when it comes to leading therapy groups, there are some common pitfalls that are important to avoid (Inaba & Cohen, 2014).

-   **Failure to have a realistic view of group treatment.** Group treatment requires a long-term perspective, so facilitators need to be patient that the group will take time to develop, especially if group treatment is a new modality in your agency or practice. Once a group forms, it can take time before they begin to function in a manner that is beneficial to members.

-   **Failure to drop the "mask" of professionalism and/or self-disclosure issues.** Neither too much disclosure nor too little disclosure is helpful. Clinicians need to be genuine in group. Be a person, not "the professional" in the group. While you still need to conduct yourself professionally, allow yourself to be a real person—don't hide behind the letters after your name; the clients in your group won't care. See the section on self-disclosure in chapter 12 for more information.

-   **Failure to understand the stages of group formation.** Groups move through different phases as they form and evolve. Your expectations for a new group should be different from those for an established group. In addition, the need for you to be directive in a group will generally be greater in new groups compared to established groups.

- **Failure to recognize countertransference issues.** In my experience, clinicians are more likely to experience countertransference in group settings compared to individual settings, mainly because you interact with more people in a group setting. Countertransference happens—it does not mean you are not a good clinician. It is important, though, to be aware of these feelings and address them in supervision.

- **Failure to clarify group rules.** The group needs rules for it to work, but as I pointed out earlier in this chapter, there should be a few rules that everyone is familiar with. Be clear with your expectations and stick to them. Group members will test the rules because they want to see how you will react. Will you take things personally and get angry? Or will you ignore the rules to avoid conflict? Most people living with SUD have experience with people in their lives who do either or both of these things. I strongly suggest you calmly set the rules and enforce them with little to no leeway.

- **Failure to use the entire group effectively by focusing on individual problem-solving.** When you spend too much time focusing on an individual member's specific concerns, you don't make effective use of the group. Instead, redirect individual questions and requests for advice back to the group.

- **Failure to plan.** Although you want to be flexible to respond to needs and issues that members bring to group, it's important to have a plan going into each group regardless of the group's formation stage. Don't wing it.

- **Failure to integrate new members into the group.** It is very important that new members feel welcomed. Think how nerve-racking it is to be the new person in any social setting. Therapeutic groups are no exception, so make it a priority to welcome new folks. I also encourage new clients to ask questions, repeating my mantra that there is no such thing as a stupid question.

- **Failure to understand interactions in the group as a metaphor for interactions outside the group.** The roles that people assume in group are often identical to those they play in their family or social circles, especially in the sense of drug-related issues. A person who is a bully in group is likely used to acting that way in their family to get their needs met. A person who is passive in group is likely passive outside of group. It is important to be aware of this, and in well-functioning groups, it can even be illuminating to point this out to group members. They can then use the safety of the group setting to practice making changes in how they interact with others.

ALCOHOLICS ANONYMOUS (AA)

AA began in 1935, and since its formation, it has inspired similar fellowships and helped millions of people (White, 2014). AA is not treatment per se, and it is not for everyone. In order for clinicians to understand this resource, I highly recommend attending several open meetings, regardless of whether you are in recovery, to understand how the fellowship works and the distinct characteristics groups can adopt. You should also check out the AA website (www.aa.org) to learn about the 12 steps and 12 traditions of AA.

The key concepts of AA are contained within *The Big Book*, which contains the writings of Bill W. and Dr. Bob (the founders of AA) plus the common themes of AA. It is made up of firsthand accounts of addiction and recovery from many people. The following are some of the core themes and principles that underlie the program:

- AA is grounded on the principle of anonymity. ("My name is _____ and I'm an alcoholic.") By having group members identify themselves by just their first name, anonymity is preserved within the group. This anonymity serves to provide privacy to members and creates a sense of a common bond among participants. The phrase "a friend of Bill" is also used as a way for people to identify themselves as being in the fellowship.

- AA holds that addiction is a disease that cannot be cured, but that people with addiction can be in perpetual recovery from the illness by not using addictive substances. Sobriety is a key component of this, and AA members often date the start of their recovery from the day they "got sober." Most AA members will know the exact date and will celebrate their anniversary annually. Most meetings provide time to recognize people who are celebrating one day (or one month, one year, or multiple years) of sobriety by giving them a coin or a key chain tag.

- AA is structured around 12 steps that people in recovery work through sequentially. They usually do this with the help of a sponsor—someone who has been in recovery longer than they have. There is no time limit to how long it takes a person to move through the steps, and many people will return to previous steps for additional "work" as they see a need. A friend of mine who is in long-term recovery focuses on a specific step each month as part of his ongoing journey.

- By helping someone else, we help ourselves. Being of service to others facilitates a sense of belonging and purpose that supports sobriety. It also helps to temporarily take the focus off the individual's own struggles. Individuals in AA surrender themselves to a higher power—to anything greater than themselves. Many clients are bothered by this, especially if the focus is on God and they either do not believe in God or have experienced spiritual abuse. I ask members to consider anything greater than themselves. There are also secular 12 step-programs (W, 2018).

- In AA, the focus is on staying in recovery one day at a time, or "just for today." This is an acknowledgment that sobriety is very difficult, so rather than promising never to use again, the idea is to focus on the day (or even hour) that is before you and not become obsessed with the future.

- AA views recovery as a transformational process and a lifestyle change that is greater than sobriety alone. This is similar to what I have written in this book; recovery is more than just not using substances. It is an ongoing journey to become a better, more actualized person.

OTHER 12-STEP GROUPS

Al-Anon	Methadone Anonymous
Ala-teen	Millati Islami
Celebrate Recovery	Narcotics Anonymous
Cocaine Anonymous	Over-Eaters Anonymous
Double-Trouble Recovery	Pills Anonymous
Gamblers Anonymous	Secular Organizations for Recovery
Medication-Assisted Recovery Anonymous	Sexaholics Anonymous

There are many advantages to 12-step groups in that they create a sense of community and provide resources for the client. Groups are free, are offered in a variety of settings and at various times, and are tailored for specific populations (e.g., male only, female only, etc.). By interacting with others experiencing the same struggles, peers give credibility and provide examples of possible and sustainable recovery by people just like them. And by helping others, clients also work on their own recovery. I highly recommend that you check out Narcotics Anonymous (www.na.org), which has a section for professionals you may find helpful.

However, 12-step groups can have several weaknesses in that some groups can be dogmatic, with an emphasis on labels and negative self-talk. Members can also be discouraged from treating co-occurring mental illnesses with medication (or psychotherapy) or from engaging in medication-assisted treatment. In addition, as with any group format, the group setting can trigger trauma reactions in some clients. The possibility of predation exists within the group as well, especially toward newer members who can be vulnerable.

First Step Exercise

The road to recovery begins when you admit that you have a problem and you admit your powerlessness over drugs or alcohol. This represents the first step in AA: "We admitted we are powerless over alcohol—that our lives had become unmanageable." Use the following questions to begin to understand the scope of your SUD.

What does it mean to be powerless?

Why do you think people struggle with the term *powerless*?

What does it mean for you to be powerless over a substance or a behavior?

How has your life become unmanageable?

What happened for you to realize that your life had become unmanageable?

What is one thing you could do differently today to make your life more manageable?

SMART RECOVERY

As mentioned earlier, people may struggle with the spiritual aspects of AA and other 12-step groups. Therefore, they may be less willing to attend meetings or seek the fellowship of traditional peer support groups. In response to these concerns, a group known as Rational Recovery formed to apply secular, cognitive-based thinking to help people work their way out of their addiction. It was renamed SMART Recovery in 1994 (Hardin, 2013), which stands for:

S = self
M = management
A = and
R = recovery
T = training

SMART Recovery utilizes CBT, REBT, and MI therapies to help people change how they think about substances, thus changing their relationship with substances. It draws on the power of group meetings in combination with a four-point program of individual work to guide people toward recovery. Unlike the 12-steps of AA or NA, the points can be worked in any order.

The Four-Point Program
Building and Maintaining Motivation
Coping With Urges
Managing Thoughts, Feelings, and Behaviors
Living a Balanced Life

SMART Recovery can work as a stand-alone program or in conjunction with other programs, including AA or NA. A friend of mine regularly attends NA meetings and SMART Recovery meetings, noting that she takes the best aspects of both to work on her recovery. She does not find them mutually exclusive.

CASE EXAMPLE

For several years, I co-facilitated a group in a residential program for men with co-occurring disorders, nearly all of whom had spent time in prison for crimes such as murder, assault, drug dealing, and weapons charges. The older members often had to "break in" the "young bucks" who were first entering the program. They did so not by threatening the younger members but by caring for them and modeling acceptable behavior. I asked Ted, one of the older members, why he did this.

"Man, I am an institutionalized individual," he said.

"What's that got to do with how you're trying to help these young guys?" I asked.

"I spent 30 years in prison for some bullshit I did as a stupid kid," Ted said. "And I missed being there for my own kids. I don't know, maybe I'm trying to make up for something with these guys."

"That sounds like a real man talking," I said. "Not someone who is institutionalized."

Ted laughed, "Well, yeah, most of the time. The grown-up part of me wants to help them along. The institutionalized part of me wants to beat their ass."

"I'm glad you're keeping the two sides separate," I responded.

"It's hard," he said, still laughing.

After working with people with SUD for nearly 25 years, people still ask me why I do it. It's hard to explain when you haven't been around someone like Ted. The ability to see other people make changes in their lives, to grow toward the person they want to be, is awesome and humbling. At the end of these meetings, the guys would join hands, remember the people they knew who had died from SUD, and then say the serenity prayer. I've heard a lot of prayers in my life, but none as sincere and real as those I heard in those meetings. This kind of experience always reminds me of the power a group can have.

11

Treatment Strategies for Special Populations

Historically, SUD treatment was applied almost exclusively toward White, middle-to-upper-class heterosexual males (White, 2014). As society has evolved, we have come to acknowledge that SUD can affect anyone regardless of race, ethnicity, gender identity, socioeconomic status, sexual orientation, and so on. While there are similarities in how treatment can be provided across populations, there are differences in how to operationalize SUD with groups based upon their unique needs.

In this chapter, we will look at the needs of various groups when it comes to SUD treatment. This information presents broad views of complex and varied groups, but keep in mind that every person is unique, and we occupy different groups simultaneously. Therefore, treatment should always be individualized.

WOMEN

In the early 1900s, SUD treatment approaches were ignorant of women's specific needs, and they were not subject to the same standards used with men. As a result, women often found themselves placed in psychiatric institutions as opposed to specialized SUD treatment programs (White, 2014). Research from the past three decades shows notable differences in how SUD has impacted women, providing implications for treatment. The following list highlights some of the features of women with SUD compared to men with SUD (Frances et al., 2005; SAMHSA, 2020).

Differences in SUD Among Women, Compared to Men

- Women drink less but reach a higher blood alcohol level within a shorter time.

- Women generally develop SUD later in life and it progresses more rapidly (known as "telescoping"), with negative health consequences developing faster as well.

- Women are more likely to drink alone.

- Women with SUD have a higher mortality rate and are more likely to die from cirrhosis of the liver, circulatory disease, suicide, or accidents related to SUD.

- Women with SUD are more likely to have a significant other with SUD.

- Women with SUD have higher rates of comorbid mental illnesses (particularly depression, anxiety, trauma, and eating disorders) and are more likely to attempt suicide.

- Women are more likely to have a history of physical and sexual abuse.

- Women more often date the onset of pathological alcohol or drug use to a specific stressful event.

- Women are less likely to seek drug treatment and more likely to initially seek mental health treatment.

Given the unique differences that women experience, there are several important factors to consider when applying SUD treatment to women (Frances et al., 2005). The first is that providing trauma-informed care is absolutely necessary, as the correlation between trauma and SUD is very high. Providers must pay attention to trauma history and assess for current risk of physical or sexual assault. Clients may also need assistance to escape (or prepare to escape) from an abusive significant other.

Remember that we are treating the whole person, not just their SUD. Therefore, it is necessary to conduct a comprehensive physical examination to assess for physical complications and medical disorders (which aligns with the assessment criteria outlined by ASAM). This includes assessing the client's access to health care, including seeing an obstetrician-gynecologist (OB-GYN). Given that women are more likely to be primary caregivers for minor children, they may require additional case management, and it is critical that their housing, transportation, employment, childcare, and parenting needs be continually assessed throughout treatment. Evaluation and treatment of significant others and children is also important.

When working with women in traditionally underserved groups, such as sexual minorities, racial and ethnic minorities, and those with justice system involvement, it can be helpful to provide them time to work with positive female role models with similar experiences (such as treatment staff or peer counselors). Finally, given that clients may have been subjected to the effects of sexism in previous treatment experiences, from both peers and professionals alike, some clients may benefit from women-only treatment programs.

PREGNANT CLIENTS

Drug use during pregnancy is an all-too-common reality that many treatment providers will encounter, with about 20 percent of infants being exposed to alcohol at some point during gestation and 15 percent of pregnant clients smoking tobacco during pregnancy (Inaba & Cohen, 2014). In addition, many clients do not even realize they are pregnant until at least halfway through the first trimester, if not later. Therefore, pregnancy screening during the assessment and throughout treatment is imperative. Clients should also be reminded that their baby is vulnerable at *any stage* of pregnancy. The following table describes some of the negative consequences of various substances used during pregnancy.

Alcohol	<ul><li>Alcohol use during pregnancy is the leading cause of intellectual disability in the U.S.</li><li>Fetal alcohol syndrome is the third most common birth defect.</li><li>Alcohol use increases the risk of miscarriage, placental separation, premature labor, and infant death.</li><li>The rate of sudden infant death syndrome increases if a client drinks while pregnant or nursing.</li></ul>
Stimulants	<ul><li>Stimulant use during pregnancy can cause placental separation, increased fetal activity, and premature labor.</li><li>At birth, infants can experience withdrawal syndrome that includes increased respiration, agitation, hyperactivity, seizures, tremulousness, sensitivity to light and touch, and problems with sucking or swallowing.</li></ul>
Opioids	<ul><li>Opioid use during pregnancy can cause infants to be born with neonatal opioid withdrawal syndrome (NOWS), characterized by high-pitched crying, tremors, frequent yawning, vomiting, sweating, fever, and problems with eating, sleeping, and breathing.</li><li>Infants with NOWS are typically admitted to a neonatal intensive unit, where 60%–80% require pharmacological treatment (McQueen & Murphy-Oikonen, 2016).</li><li>A pregnant client who stops using opioids "cold turkey" has a greater risk of miscarriage, so they are strongly encouraged to start, or continue, medication-assisted therapy (e.g., Suboxone).</li></ul>

Given that psychoactive drugs can negatively impact the developing fetus more than the mother, many clients are reluctant to seek SUD treatment (and sometimes even prenatal care) when pregnant because they are fearful of legal (or other punitive) consequences should they disclose their pregnancy. Compounding this is a lack of programs exclusively for pregnant clients with SUD.

One solution is to make SUD treatment more available, particularly in OB-GYN settings. In fact, a number of OB-GYN providers have become SUD treatment providers, with some adding this service when the Drug Addiction Treatment Act of 2000 provided them with the ability to prescribe buprenorphine. This has decreased stigma and increased treatment access in some communities. Another solution is to tailor treatment programs to specifically serve pregnant and parenting clients, including residential, partial hospitalization, and outpatient treatment programs. These types of programs would be beneficial, as clients have reported feeling judged by non-pregnant peers in mixed treatment settings.

On the next pages, you'll find two different scales that were developed to screen women for risky alcohol use during pregnancy—the TWEAK (which is named by an acronym for *tolerance, worried, eye-opener, amnesia, and k/cut down* [Russell, 1994]) and the T-ACE (which uses questions from the CAGE screening while also adding *tolerance for alcohol* [Sokol et al., 1989]).

TWEAK*

	Question	Score**
Tolerance	How many drinks can you hold? 0 to 2 drinks = 0 points 3 or more drinks = 2 points	
Worried	Have close friends or relatives worried or complained about your drinking in the past year? Yes = 2 point	
Eye-opener	Do you sometimes take a drink in the morning when you first get up? Yes = 1 point	
Amnesia (blackouts)	Has a friend or family member ever told you about things you said or did while you were drinking that you could not remember? Yes = 1 point	
K/Cut down	Do you sometimes feel the need to cut down on your drinking? Yes = 1 point	

---

* Russell, M. (1994). New assessment tools for drinking in pregnancy: T-ACE, TWEAK, and others. *Alcohol Health and Research World*, 18(1), 55–61.

** A total score of 2 or more indicates a high risk of alcohol misuse during pregnancy.

T-ACE*

	Question	Score**
Tolerance	How many drinks does it take to make you feel high? 0 to 2 drinks = 0 points 3 or more drinks = 2 points	
Annoyed	Have people annoyed you by criticizing your drinking? Yes = 1 point	
Cut down	Have you ever felt you ought to cut down on your drinking? Yes = 1 point	
Eye-opener	Have you ever had a drink first thing in the morning to steady your nerves or to get rid of a hangover? Yes = 1 point	

---

* Sokol, R. J., Martier, S. S., & Ager, J. W. (1989). The T-ACE questions: Practical prenatal detection of risk-drinking. *American Journal of Obstetrics and Gynecology, 160*(4), 863–870.

** A total score of 2 or more indicates a positive outcome for risky drinking during pregnancy.

ADOLESCENTS

Although SUD treatment for adolescents began by mimicking adult treatment, it soon became apparent that applying adult treatment approaches to adolescents was rarely effective (White, 2017). As we continue to learn more about neurological development, we can see why there is often a disconnect between adolescents and established adult SUD treatment. In particular, the prefrontal cortex—the area of the human brain associated with impulse control, judgment, and decision-making—does not fully develop until about age 25. In contrast, more primitive areas of the brain develop earlier, meaning that adolescence is a time when cravings and emotions related to drugs are strong, but ways to regulate those impulses have yet to develop.

Given that adolescents can be resistant to treatment, MI techniques can be effective in increasing engagement during the first stages of treatment. Once you've established rapport, many clients respond to individual CBT, structured family therapy, or therapeutic groups. However, with group treatment, composition is extremely important; expect more acting out and direct opposition from adolescents compared to adults. You'll find that rolling with resistance and limit-setting is an ongoing process in the group.

To the extent possible, you'll want to schedule treatment so it does not negatively impact the school day. Parental involvement is also key and is almost always linked to better treatment outcomes. And above all, be genuine to who you are and don't fall into the trap of trying to be "cool." Teenagers can easily see through that.

The next few pages provide you with some tools for working with adolescents. I also recommend using the CRAFFT Questionnaire (*car, relax, alone, forget, friends, trouble*) to assess for risky drug use, which is a valid assessment tool for young clients ages 12 to 21. The questionnaire can be found at https://crafft.org.

"What Do You Want to Do?"

Many of you have been sent to treatment by your parents, guardians, or the court system, and you don't want to be here. It is okay to feel that way. But since you are here, use the following questions so we can start a conversation about how I can help you.

Why are you in treatment?

Who do you feel has power in (or over) your life?

What decision-making abilities do you have?

What is going well for you?

What would you like to see change?

Describe your relationships with substances:

How do they help you?

Do they hurt you in any way?

What has changed in your life because of your substance use?

How does your family see you?

How do you see your family?

What do you want to do in treatment?

Evaluating Risks and Rewards

Decisions have consequences, and one way to determine which choices you make is to visualize the potential outcome of your decisions. Use the following questions to help you examine the decisions you have made or could make.

Think of something you want to do. What is it?

Why do you want to do this?

List out all the rewards (good things) that could happen if you do this.

List out all the risks (potential bad things) that could happen if you do this.

Does this choice have more risks or rewards associated with it? How does that impact your decision?

How can you apply this decision-making process to other situations?

RACIAL AND ETHNIC MINORITIES

Minority populations have historically been underserved in SUD treatment, in part due to the heterogenic nature (i.e., White, middle-to-upper-class males) of SUD treatment until recently. Racism has also played a significant role in determining which substances are legal and which are not. Indeed, the war on drugs—or more appropriately, the war on people who use drugs—has been largely fought against people in minority and low socioeconomic communities for its entire existence. For example, crack cocaine, which is disproportionally used by racial minorities, especially Black people, has historically been associated with harsher mandatory sentencing laws than powdered cocaine.

In addition to disparities in drug treatment and drug policy, wider disparities in overall health care access create barriers to treatment in many minority communities. This issue was brought to the forefront during the COVID-19 pandemic, in which racial and ethnic minorities were found to exhibit higher rates of infection, hospitalization, and death from COVID-19, but it has existed for quite some time (Radley et al., 2021).

The following table provides an overview of some considerations when working with various racial and ethnic minority groups. If I have omitted anything important, or made a mistake in my terminology, please understand that I do so from a position of wanting to be helpful and attract people to treatment.

Black/African American	• Black people generally have less access to quality mental health and SUD treatment. • Alcohol use tends to start slower, catching up to their White counterparts as they age (especially in men). • There is a higher incidence of medical problems (e.g., hypertension) brought on by SUD and lack of access to medical treatment. • They often exhibit higher levels of spiritual and religious involvement, which can be incorporated into treatment.
Latino/Latina/Latinx	• Men are more likely to develop alcohol use disorder due to a more permissive cultural norm that is tied to acculturation, but women are increasing their levels of drinking as well. • Opioid overdose rates in this population are increasing. • There is a lack of culturally sensitive treatment providers due to language barriers. • Family roles are important, as is interdependence, and the extended family and these themes can be incorporated into treatment.

Asian and Pacific Islander	• This population is the fastest-growing minority group in the U.S. • They have diverse religious and spiritual expressions with varying views about substance use. • Some individuals of East-Asian descent experience a facial flushing reaction following alcohol consumption, which may affect their alcohol use. • Family embarrassment and shame may lead to increased hiding of drug use (which also makes confidentiality important in treatment). • The family is often more important than the individual. • Gender roles are important, so same-sex treatment groups may be more effective.
Native Americans/ First Nations	• This population is a diverse group that comprises over 200 tribes in North America. • Alcohol use disorder is recognized as a significant problem in many tribes, but patterns vary widely among tribes. • Hallucinogenic plants are responsibly used in some Native American rituals. • A majority of tribes value self-determination and believe in the unity and sacredness of all nature. • There is a growing use of alternative methods and models of recovery that connect with traditional medicines and practices.

We sometimes struggle to understand people we perceive as being different from us, or we make assumptions about them based upon their outward appearances. I think this is a big challenge in our work, but I also think it is the most rewarding. For example, years ago, I was in a practice working with adults diagnosed with co-occurring disorders. I met a new client, Ray, who was about my age and Black, and he immediately began sizing me up. I could tell that he had noticed the crucifix tattoo I have on my right forearm as he sat down on the couch and held tightly onto his car keys.

Instead of firing off a bunch of questions to conduct my initial assessment, I tried to engage Ray in a conversation to learn more about him. Ray explained that he was depressed and drinking too much. He was gay, HIV-positive, and heartbroken over a recent relationship that had ended poorly. He had heard that I was a "gay-friendly" therapist, so he sought me out.(I had not realized that I had this reputation but was quite pleased to have found out!) After about five minutes of talking, he tossed his car keys aside. Once we completed the assessment, I asked if I had passed the "audition."

"Yeah, I think you did," Ray said, smiling.

"I thought I might have when you tossed your keys aside," I replied.

"Yeah, there was just something I needed to get over."

"What's that?" I asked. "This cross on my arm?" My assumption was that he would think I would judge him based on his sexual orientation.

"No, I'm an atheist," Ray said. "I couldn't care less if you're a Christian. I was more concerned because you're White."

I paused for a moment.

"I appreciate your honesty," I said. "As it's not something I can help."

"Any more than I can help being Black," Ray said.

"True, it's who we are," I said.

"So my question is, what can I learn from a White, Christian, straight, seronegative (HIV-negative) guy?"

"Or what can I learn from a Black, gay, seropositive, atheist?" I asked. "Why don't we find out since we've already started."

"Deal," Ray said.

That was over 10 years ago. Ray worked extremely hard in counseling and began recovering from his depression and alcohol use disorder. In our conversations, I learned a lot about his experiences as a gay, Black male in American society. The important thing is that Ray was able to define who he was to me, and he allowed me to ask questions about his experiences and how they impacted his depression and alcohol use.

Even when we examine SUD in the context of cultural differences, we need to remember that treatment should be individualized. For example, a person's community or socioeconomic status may play a larger role in their life than their ethnic identity, sexual orientation, or gender identity. We also need to be aware of cultural trends and our country's historical treatment of minority groups. Finally, we cannot understand SUD and SUD treatment without recognizing that racism and classism have been an integral part of determining which substances are acceptable or are illegal: The differences often lie in underlying societal attitudes, prejudice, and stigma rather than science.

The following group activity can help people see the complexities that form who we are as individuals. This is not an icebreaker activity and is meant to be used when there is trust among group members. Clients can share as much or as little as they feel comfortable.

Iceberg Exercise

Most of an iceberg's mass is underwater. Although we cannot see the underwater part of the iceberg, it is still there, and we know it is there. People are similar: We can tell something about a person by looking at them, but that is a small part of who that person is.

For example, if you look at me, you will see a bald, middle-aged (as of this writing) male with white skin. If you hear me speak, you will learn that I speak English. You may notice a wedding band on my left hand. Without talking with me, however, you would not understand my ethnic background, my upbringing, my education, my role as a parent, my profession as a social worker, and so forth.

This exercise challenges you to describe yourself beyond what others see. On a blank sheet of paper, draw a horizontal line (this is your water line) about one-third of the way down. Next, draw an iceberg (any oval shape will do), making sure that about one-sixth of it is above the water line. Finally, in the large area beneath the waterline, write down all the things that describe you that no one else can see without getting to know you. In the smaller area above the waterline, write down the things people can know about you based on what they see.

LGBTQ+ COMMUNITY

Understanding and appreciating the experiences of the LGBTQ+ community is imperative if clinicians are to effectively engage clients in treatment. Individuals in this community are often subjected to prejudicial treatment and made to feel ostracized regarding their sexual orientation or gender identity. Many have experienced shame and even abuse from medical providers. Therefore, it is incumbent upon you as the clinician to recognize and extinguish heteronormative and cisnormative actions and language that could push LGBTQ+ clients away. Since the language regarding gender and sexual orientation is always evolving, I encourage you to review the current glossary of terms provided by PFLAG, which is the largest organization for lesbian, gay, bisexual, transgender, and queer people and their family, friends, and allies. You can find this glossary and much more information about the organization at https://pflag.org.

In my former clinic, our triage clinician would ask clients for their name and pronouns. I have included an intake form similar to what we used in the clinic, which you can modify for your practice. At the same time, don't push the client to disclose information related to their identity or sexuality that they are not yet ready to share; instead, you should rely on open-ended questions. Understand that working toward recovery may also coincide with the person beginning or continuing their coming out process.

In addition, given the discrimination and violence perpetrated against LGBTQ+ individuals, substance use occurs at higher rates among this population (SAMHSA, 2020), as clients may use alcohol or other drugs to dissociate or numb themselves. Therefore, it is important to take an overall trauma-informed approach in the initial stages of treatment, coupled with MI strategies to address any ambivalence about SUD treatment. It is also imperative that you ensure your client is in a safe living environment.

Once you have established a strong therapeutic relationship, consider a CBT or psychodynamic approach to address SUD. Family of origin issues (which may or may not include family therapy) may need to be addressed once the client is engaged in treatment, though family therapy is contraindicated if the family is violent or otherwise toxic. In addition, if your client is interested in attending a 12-step program for their SUD, there are 12-step rainbow programs that are tailored for LGBTQ+ members and their allies. Above all, do your best to create a safe space for the client, use inclusive language, and refrain from making assumptions. Remember that the client is the expert of their own experience.

Intake Form

Legal name:

_____

Name you use (if different from your legal name):

_____

Pronouns:

_____   He/him/his

_____   She/her/hers

_____   They/them/theirs

_____   Other: _____

Gender: (Feel free to leave this blank if you wish)

_____   Male

_____   Female

_____   Nonbinary

_____   Male to female transgender

_____   Female to male transgender

_____   Other: _____

PEOPLE WITH DISABILITIES

People with disabilities are often not seen by members of the larger culture, especially as we tend to determine a person's worth based on what they can do as opposed to who they are. Some disabilities are visible (e.g., a person using a wheelchair), while others may not be readily apparent (e.g., a person who is deaf or who has an intellectual disability). We must remember that just because a person has a disability does not make them immune from having a SUD; in fact, it may place them at risk of developing a SUD (CSAT, 2015).

One of the most important things we need to consider when working with clients with physical disabilities is access. Consider the accessibility of your clinic, including whether you have accessible parking spaces, wheelchair ramps, and accessible restroom facilities. Provide accommodation as necessary. If you receive federal funding of any kind, you are required to provide accommodations. This includes visual aids for people who are blind and sign-language interpretation for clients who are deaf.

In addition, individuals with certain cognitive disabilities may require a longer interview, and rest periods may need to be scheduled. Make sure to build in flexibility to your intake and treatment sessions, allowing sessions to be shortened, lengthened, or made more frequent, depending on the individual treatment plan.

Above all, it is important to remember that people are more than their disabilities, just as any person living with SUD is more than their addiction. Avoid making assumptions about what a person can or cannot do based on their disabilities. Whenever possible, focus on the person's strengths and adaptive capabilities.

PEOPLE EXPERIENCING HOMELESSNESS

Although homelessness has long been associated with SUD, many people who lack housing do not have SUD—in fact, most people with SUD are not homeless. However, for individuals with SUD who are homeless, there may be sober living houses available (now usually called recovery houses), which can be helpful for those who are highly motivated to maintain their sobriety. These houses provide a safe environment where individuals rebuild their lives as they transition to more independent living.

Recovery houses are typically staffed by people with lived experiences in recovery. Some facilities meet the ASAM level 3.1 criteria of a residential treatment program (clinically managed low-intensity residential), while others offer basic amenities in a drug-free environment. Clients in recovery houses are usually expected to work (there is often a network of employers willing to hire clients who are new to recovery), help with upkeep of the home (e.g., doing basic cleaning or cooking), and attend peer support groups or treatment. The length of stay can vary from months to well over a year.

One of the weaknesses of many recovery houses is their tendency to kick out people if they use substances, which can be problematic. In response, the Housing First approach has emerged, which maintains clients experiencing homelessness need to find safe, stable housing *before* they can address other problems in their lives, such as their SUD. This approach is based on the notion that clients need to have access to basic necessities, like physical shelter, first and foremost. Ideally, a Housing First approach should be integrated with a program that addresses medical care, mental health, SUD, dental care, vocational training, and other coordinated services that are client-centered to help clients maintain housing (and recovery). It is imperative that you remain up to date about the services in your community for clients struggling with housing. Most Housing First agencies are connected with other organizations that provide medical, mental health, and SUD treatment.

MILITARY PERSONNEL

Deployed personnel face extreme violence, extended periods out of communication with their families, and difficult living situations while their families and loved ones live with anxiety, fear, and worry. As a result, there are high rates of PTSD among active and veteran personnel, including at least 20 percent of clients with comorbid SUD. However, treatment is often complicated by the fact that many agencies for the armed services are understaffed or lack clinicians able to provide SUD treatment. In addition, there is continued bias among military personnel about substance use and SUD treatment, including fears among many active members that seeking help will negatively impact their careers.

Therefore, when treating military clients, you should familiarize yourself with military culture (both in general and about any specific installations near your practice), and be knowledgeable about services for military personnel in your area, including housing, employment, financial, and other case management needs. Given the higher incidence of PTSD in this community (including among family members), it is imperative to use a trauma-informed approach and to conduct ongoing suicide screenings. Clinicians should also address the issue of guns, as knowledge of firearms is part of the client's work. Ask specific questions about how they store their weapons and ammunition, and if you have concerns about lethality, discuss this with the client and explore how to remove the weapon or limit access.

OLDER ADULTS

People over the age of 65 are the fastest-growing age group in the United States. Oftentimes, the idea of substance use among elderly clients is not considered by health care providers—causing them to minimize or dismiss the idea altogether—but individuals of all ages can struggle with substance use. Among older adults, alcohol, prescription opioids, and benzodiazepines are the most frequently used drugs.

When treating older adults with SUD, it is important to consider that many elderly people are on multiple medications for varying medical issues, which complicates the impact of any drug. Age-related physiological changes can potentiate the effects of drug and alcohol toxicity as well. Unfortunately, many health professionals have inadequate training on geriatric medication and SUD, so substance use is often misdiagnosed as dementia or another mental health problem like depression (which itself is underdiagnosed among the elderly). As a general rule, conduct a comprehensive medical workup at the start of treatment to identify and address any comorbid medical issues.

In addition, any form of treatment must address aging-related issues, such as grief, loss, loneliness, and loss of independence. Be honest with the client by stating that you believe they have a substance use problem, even though this might create resistance from them or their family. Group therapy, including groups that consist of other seniors and in which SUD is not the central theme, has been shown to be an effective tool, as the social support provided by the group can counter the loneliness that often occurs with older adults.

OVERALL CONSIDERATIONS

When working with people who are different from us, it is important to remain open-minded and ready to learn from others. It is equally important that we keep any preconceived notions we might have in check. This includes being aware of our own biases (we all have them) and confronting those biases when we recognize them. Finally, if you make a mistake (we're all human), own it, fix it, and learn from it moving forward. The following chart describes the most important concepts to remember when working with clients that are different from you.

Recognize	your biases and confront or adjust them as needed
Do not make	assumptions about a client based on their age, race, ethnicity, gender, ability, sexual orientation, etc.
Conduct	a thorough assessment
Avoid	stereotyping, and develop individualized treatment plans for each client
Ask	if you have a question
Own it	if you make a mistake and apologize

12

Legal and Ethical Issues in SUD Treatment

Effective SUD treatment utilizes a team of professionals, each with their own licensing boards, areas of expertise, and codes of ethics. Given the nature of this interdisciplinary treatment approach, team members need to have an understanding not only of each other's roles but also the ethical obligations that each person should follow. For example, a social worker may be legally and ethically required to report certain situations to authorities that a physician or peer recovery specialist would not be required to report. In this chapter, I'll examine some ethical and legal considerations that should guide your decision-making so you can provide the best care, all while protecting your clients, your profession, and society at large.

CORE ETHICAL PRINCIPLES

Regardless of one's profession, SUD providers should strive to have a consistent ethical standard. For example, ASAM has established the following core ethical principles (Herron & Brennan, 2015):

1. **Autonomy:** The client has a right to make decisions for themselves, even if we do not agree with their decisions. Our role is to make sure the client understands the potential consequences of their actions.

2. **Beneficence:** We are morally obligated to act in the best interest of the client. There can be limits to this, though, especially when we consider the client's right to autonomy.

3. **Nonmaleficence:** Our obligation is to do no harm to the client and to provide treatments that are not harmful. We must also inform the client of any risks of the treatment.

4. **Justice:** At the macro level, goods and services should be distributed fairly. At the micro level, all clients should be treated equally.

5. **Fidelity:** We must tell the truth and maintain confidentiality.

No matter what your profession is—whether you're a doctor, nurse, counselor, or peer recovery specialist—it is imperative that you adhere to these principles.

THERAPIST SELF-DISCLOSURE

The question of self-disclosure is an ethical dilemma that clinicians often grapple with. They may fear being asked about their own addiction or recovery history or whether they have personal experience with SUD. Clinicians with a history of SUD may not want to disclose their past experiences to clients, while those without such history may feel like their lack of experience will interfere with their ability to build rapport with clients. Clinicians may also fear that clients will doubt their ability to empathize with their experience without having gone through their own struggles with substance use (Danzer, 2019).

When considering when (and when not) to self-disclose, understand that some degree of self-disclosure is inevitable. When we interact with others, we naturally convey something about ourselves through the way we talk, dress, and carry ourselves. At the same time, the use of self-disclosure should be a planned, thoughtful decision. It should always benefit the client, and not be used to meet your needs, so when you're considering whether to share something about yourself, ask *why* you feel compelled to share this information. Supervision can also help you determine the potential pros and cons of sharing.

When it comes to deciding whether to answer one of the most feared questions—"Are you in recovery?"—your first reaction might be to respond with either a yes or a no. However, consider this possible alternative: "That's a fair question and I will answer it, but what will my answer mean to you? What if I say yes? What if I say no?" (Danzer, 2019, p. 132). At the end of the day, though, don't worry too much about whether you choose to disclose your own recovery. If it helps you to be less caught off guard when this question inevitably comes up, you can practice your answer so you are ready when the time comes. Most of the time, however, there isn't going to be a likely impact on the treatment relationship if you answer the previous question in the negative or if you answer indirectly. Ultimately, treatment outcomes are the same whether you have personal experience with SUD or not (White, 2017).

What Will You Say?

As a clinician working with clients with SUD, it is inevitable that at some point, one of your clients will ask you some iteration of the following questions:

> **"Have you used the drugs I use?"**
>
> **"Do you have SUD?"**
>
> **"Are you in recovery?"**

Before responding, consider the following:

1. Why is this client asking you this question?

2. What are some positive ways your response could impact the client?

3. What are some negative ways your response could impact the client?

4. Are you certain your disclosure is about the client and not you? (Think this over carefully.)

5. What could you say?

CLIENT CONFIDENTIALITY

Client confidentiality is the key to effective SUD treatment. In order to uphold confidentiality, it is important to understand the privacy laws that govern SUD treatment, why consent to treatment is important, and what to include in a release of information.

PRIVACY LAWS

There are two primary federal laws governing client confidentiality: the Health Insurance Portability and Accountability Act (HIPAA) and Title 42 of the Code of Federal Regulations (42 CFR) Part 2 (Seitz & Waterman, 2020). HIPAA establishes standards for the protection of general health information, whereas 42 CFR Part 2 covers enhanced privacy for certain SUD treatment. Each law is described in greater detail in the following table.

HIPAA	42 CFR Part 2
• Applies to covered entities (most health care providers, health plans, and their related business associates) • Protects the privacy and security of protected health information (PHI) • Provides certain rights to clients • Protects health data integrity, confidentiality, and accessibility • Permits disclosures without client consent for treatment, payment, and health care operations	• Applies to "Part 2" programs (federally assisted SUD treatment programs and most recipients of Part 2 records) • Protects privacy and security of records that identify individuals as seeking/receiving SUD treatment (this is to encourage people to enter and remain in SUD treatment) • Requires consent for treatment, payment, and health care operations, with limited exceptions • Proposed changes are being vetted to better support coordinated care among SUD treatment providers—some recently implemented, with more sweeping changes coming

If your program is governed by both HIPAA and 42 CFR Part 2, follow the law that is most protective of client privacy. In most cases, 42 CFR Part 2 is more protective. Some states have laws that provide even greater protection, and if you serve clients in these states, you should follow the more protective law.

Is My Program a 42 CFR Part 2 Program?

YES, if your program is any of one of the following:

- The program is **federally assisted** (receives federal funds, support, assistance, or authorization). This includes being granted IRS tax-exempt status or allowing tax deductions for contributions to the program.

- The program **provides SUD services** (diagnosis, treatment, or referral for treatment for a SUD).

- The program **holds itself out as a program that provides SUD services.** This applies if your program advertises itself (either to the community or online) as a SUD program, is state-licensed as a SUD treatment provider, is listed in SUD treatment registries, holds certifications in SUD treatment, or consults with other SUD practitioners.

- The program **has a primary function to provide SUD treatment.** However, the concept of a "primary" function is not defined in regulations or in official guidance.

INFORMED CONSENT

Informed consent should be obtained in writing prior to the start of any SUD treatment. This does not simply involve getting the client to sign a consent form. Rather, it is necessary to verbally review all aspects of the form with the client prior to starting treatment to ensure they understand (1) what is expected in treatment and (2) the limits of what you can and cannot disclose without their permission. Informed consent has three components:

1. **Knowledge** of the treatment, options, risks, and alternatives

2. **Competency**—the client has the cognitive ability to make rational decisions and understand the treatment and potential risks associated with it

3. V**oluntary acceptance**

A key component of informed consent is explaining to the client what treatment will take place, what is required of the client, what services you will provide, and any risk associated with treatment. As part of confirmed consent, you must also explain any exceptions to client confidentiality. For examples, clinicians have a mandated duty to report instances of abuse or neglect against a child (or vulnerable adult), as well as instances in which a client poses a danger to themselves or others. In my own practice, I also take care to explain things that are not allowed on clinic property (e.g., alcohol or illicit substances) and make it clear that law enforcement may be called in these situations. I emphasize that in any of these scenarios, the safety of the client and others takes precedence over all other considerations.

When obtaining informed consent with clients with SUD, it is crucial to consider the client's ability (i.e., competency) to provide informed consent if they are intoxicated. If the client is intoxicated, or you suspect the client is intoxicated, they cannot provide informed consent. Likewise, if the client is not intoxicated and refuses to provide informed consent, I do not provide treatment. In either case, if the client appears to be a danger to themselves or may be in danger from the effects of a substance (either due to intoxication or withdrawal syndromes), I refer them to the emergency room. Informed consent is not required in most situations involving emergency treatment.

Finally, some clients are court-ordered to receive treatment, so they may question whether they can voluntarily accept treatment. I point out that they can consent to treatment should they choose, and that if they refuse treatment (which is their right), they may simply face sanctions from the legal system.

Release of Information

It is necessary to obtain a written release of information from your client before disclosing any information regarding them (i.e., their name, address, social security number, or similar information) that could be linked back to them. Clients have the right to revoke any consent to disclosure at any time, and oral revocations must be honored. However, clients need to understand that information may be disclosed to qualified service organizations (QSO), such as a third-party billing service, but that only the minimum information needed for the QSO to do its job will be disclosed. In addition, client information can be disclosed due to a medical emergency, but the Part 2 program must document in the client's record the name and affiliation of the recipient of the information, the name of the person making the disclosure, the date and time of the disclosure and the nature of the emergency (Confidentiality of Substance Use Disorder Patient Records § 2.51, 2020).

Although releases of information are critical in ensuring client confidentiality, there are instances in which a release of information is not necessary. In particular, federal rules permit disclosures in the following circumstances (Herron & Brennan, 2015):

- When a client signs a consent form that complies with the regulations' requirements

- When a disclosure does not identify the client as an individual with a SUD

- When treatment staff consult among themselves (includes systems of care)

- When the disclosure is to a "qualified service organization" that provides services to the client

- When there is a medical emergency

- When the law requires reporting of child abuse or neglect

- When a client commits a crime at the treatment program or against its staff members

- When the information is for research, audit, or evaluation purposes

- When a court issues a special order authorizing disclosure

Required Components for a Release of Information Form*

1. The name of the patient

2. The specific name(s) or general designation(s) of the Part 2 program(s), entity(ies), or individual(s) permitted to make the disclosure

3. How much and what kind of information is to be disclosed, including an explicit description of the SUD information that may be disclosed

4. The name(s) of the individual(s) to whom a disclosure is to be made—listing the name of the legal entity receiving the information is permissible

5. The purpose of the disclosure: In accordance with 2.13(a), the disclosure must be limited to that information which is necessary to carry out the stated purpose

6. A statement that the consent is subject to revocation at any time except to the extent that the Part 2 program or other lawful holder of patient identifying information that is permitted to make the disclosure has already acted in reliance on it. Acting in reliance includes the provision of treatment services in reliance on a valid consent to disclose information to a third-party payer

7. The date, event, or condition upon which the consent will expire if not revoked before. This date, event, or condition must ensure that the consent will last no longer than necessary to serve the purpose for which it is provided

8. The signature of the client and, when required for a client who is a minor or for a patient who is incompetent or deceased, the signature of an individual authorized to sign

9. The date on which the consent is signed

* (Confidentiality of Substance Use Disorder Patient Records § 2.31, 2020; Manatt, 2020)

CLIENTS INVOLVED IN THE LEGAL SYSTEM

The link between SUD and the legal system is well-established, even as federal and state governments reassess laws for excessive prison terms for drug possession. For example, 85 percent of incarcerated individuals report drug use prior to being detained (Borowski et al., 2020), and approximately 50 to 90 percent of people who inject drugs have been incarcerated previously (ASAM, 2020). In addition, prisoners often have access to substances while incarcerated, and some clients have even told me that it is easier to obtain drugs in prison than outside. This has led some systems to use medication for opioid use disorder within the prison system.

Another major concern is what happens when people are released from incarceration. They will undoubtedly face many challenges, including the following:

- Obtaining housing (having a criminal record can limit their options)

- Getting their driver's license restored (some states restrict driving privileges while people are under court supervision or have outstanding court costs)

- Getting mental health, medical, dental, and SUD treatment services

- Obtaining medical insurance

- Getting a job

These challenges have been found to lead to a substantial increase in death rates during the first two weeks following a client's release from long-term incarceration, with overdose being the most common cause of death (Joudrey et al., 2019). In addition to increased lethality rates, clients wind up being reincarcerated at a higher rate when there is a lack of treatment. To address the needs of people during incarceration and after release, SAMHSA (2017) developed the APIC (*assess, plan, identify, coordinate*) Model as a framework for best practices regarding reentry into the community.

The APIC Model	
Assess the individual's clinical and social needs and public safety risk	• Screen clients at intake for mental health and SUD issues. • Those clients who need mental health and/or SUD treatment should be further assessed by a clinician. • Strengths and protective factors, along with criminal involvement risk, should be assessed. • Clients should be re-assessed for services prior to being released or being placed in a less-restrictive setting.
Plan for the treatment and services required to address the individual's needs, both in custody and upon reentry	• Clients requiring mental health and/or SUD treatment should be provided with treatment while in custody. • Treatment should be individualized and based on level of need. • This includes medication for opioid use disorder. • Pregnant clients should be prioritized for treatment. • Social and community support needs (e.g., housing, employment) should be identified before any transition into the community.
Identify required community and correctional programs responsible for post-release services	• Anticipate that the first hours, days, and weeks following release from incarceration will be the most difficult for clients and identify needs well before any transition into the community. • Develop and maintain relationships with appropriate community providers that can serve clients involved in the legal system.
Coordinate the transition plan to ensure implementation and avoid gaps in care with community-based services	• Provide assessment and treatment information for community providers so treatment plans can be established before the client's transition into the community. • Address transportation, health insurance, and other issues prior to the first appointment. • Evaluate the efficacy of these systems of care on a regular basis.

DRUG TREATMENT COURTS

Drug treatment courts were developed in the 1980s as a response to the growing number of people being prosecuted for drug use and possession. Over the years, this model has evolved to include families and juveniles, and it has also been applied to other societal issues (e.g., mental health, prostitution). Violent defendants are typically excluded. Upon successful completion of the program, clients may have their charges dropped, records expunged, or sentences reduced. However, failure to follow program expectations typically results in incarceration. Research has demonstrated the efficacy of drug treatment courts, particularly to decrease incarceration of nonviolent clients.

Drug treatment courts use a team-based approach that focuses on rehabilitation and recovery as opposed to punishment. They incentivize involvement in prosocial activities, such as staying in school or working, to avoid incarceration. Positive behavior is recognized and rewarded, while program violations are sanctioned. To implement this approach, drug courts are highly structured with clear expectations for clients. While the judge is the team leader, they rely on a unique partnership with all team members, including the following:

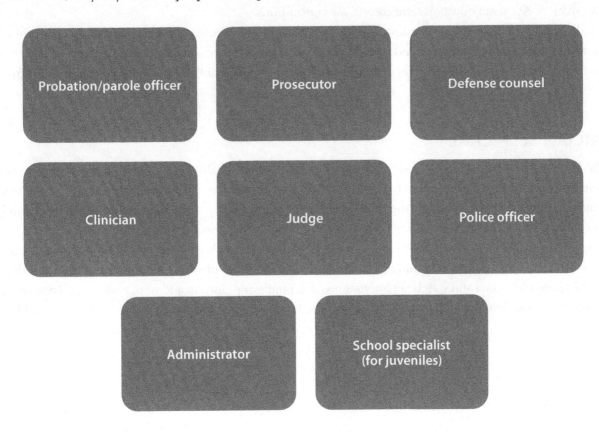

I had the honor of being part of an exceptional juvenile drug treatment court from 2003 to 2010. I saw many young people get an opportunity to make positive changes in their lives, avoiding long-term incarceration and a felony record. I also learned a lot from attorneys, police officers, and court officers, all of whom made me a better person.

CONFRONTING STIGMA

As stated throughout the book, SUD is the most stigmatized of all the psychiatric disorders, with a variety of negative stereotypes and attitudes about individuals with substance use:

- Substance use problems are the result of a moral failing.

- People with SUD are bad, lazy, dangerous people.

- If people with SUD had more willpower, they'd be able to get over it.

- People with SUD will never get better.

- Clients with SUD are resistant and difficult to work with.

As a clinician, the first thing you can do to confront stigma is to pay attention to the language you use (Avery & Avery, 2019). This is where the use of person-centered language, discussed in chapter 1, becomes important. In addition to changing how you talk, it is important to stay up to date on the latest information regarding SUD. Take opportunities to learn from your clients by listening to them. If something comes up that you are unfamiliar with, ask questions. Additionally, if you hear other providers make erroneous statements, gently correct their misinformation. Ask them questions and correct misconceptions.

Finally, when you have the opportunity to talk with other people about your work with SUD, do so! Point out that any of us can develop SUD. Remind them that people with SUD are some of the most creative and resilient people in our communities; they need help, not blame. Remember, it is not about "them" versus "us." We are all in this together.

CLINICIAN SELF-CARE

Let's be honest: This is challenging work. When we first entered the health care profession, most of us were told to carve out time to take care of ourselves—that caring for ourselves is as important as caring for our clients. Although these words are easy to say, they are sometimes hard to live by, and if we are not careful, we can burn out. It can be challenging to work in this field, and it's only possible if you care for yourself first.

Regardless of the ways you practice self-care—whether it's through exercise, meditation, yoga, art, and so forth—make sure to develop and maintain a healthy existence outside of work. Be mindful of the ways that you carry other people's trauma and watch out for your own burnout symptoms. In addition, seek supervision regularly, get counseling for yourself when you need to, and remind yourself every day why you do this work. Good luck on this journey.

Self-Care Plan

What are some things you can do daily to care for yourself?

What are some things you can do weekly to care for yourself?

What are some things you can do monthly to care for yourself?

What are some things you can do annually to care for yourself?

About the Author

Paul Brasler, LCSW, CAIP, is the owner of Providence Consulting & Education, LLC in Virginia, where he provides clinical supervision and professional education services. Brasler became an LCSW in 2002 and has extensive experience working with adults and adolescents living with substance use disorder and co-occurring disorders. He maintains a private practice and has worked in community mental health clinics, hospital emergency departments, a juvenile drug treatment court, ketamine-assisted psychotherapy, and adolescent residential treatment.

Brasler has also been presenter with PESI since 2016 and offers classes on mental health emergencies, high-risk clients, and substance use disorder treatments across the county. His first book, *High Risk Clients: Evidence-based Assessment & Clinical Tools to Recognize and Effectively Respond to Mental Health Crises*, was published with PESI in August 2019. He lives in Richmond, Virginia, with his wife and three sons, their dog, and a rabbit with serious attitude problem.

References

For your convenience, purchasers can download and print the worksheets from www.pesi.com/SUD

American Psychiatric Association. (2013). *Diagnostic and statistical manual of mental disorders* (5th ed.). https://doi.org/10.1176/appi.books.9780890425596.

American Society of Addiction Medicine. (2020). The ASAM national practice guideline for the treatment of opioid use disorder: 2020 focused update. *Journal of Addiction Medicine, 14*(S2), 1–91. https://doi.org/10.1097/ADM.0000000000000633.

Anderson, C. E., & Loomis, G. A. (2003). Recognition and prevention of inhalant abuse. *American Family Physician, 68*(5), 869–874.

Andraka-Christou, B. (2020). *The opioid fix: America's addiction crisis and the solution they don't want you to have.* John Hopkins University Press.

Avery, J. D., & Avery, J. J. (Eds.). (2019). *The stigma of addiction: An essential guide.* Springer Publishing.

Bacon, M. (2019). *Family therapy and the treatment of substance use disorders: The family matters model.* Routledge.

Borowski, S., Wenzel, S., Smith, L., & Turner, S. (2020). An evaluation of the community recovery program: A case management approach to assisting individuals recover from substance use and incarceration. *Journal of Psychosocial Rehabilitation and Mental Health, 7*(2), 149–160.

Boyle, S. W., Hull, G. H., Mather, J. H., Smith, L. L., & Farley, O. W. (2009). *Direct practice in social work* (2nd ed.). Pearson.

Brasler, P. (2019). *High risk clients: Evidence-based assessment & clinical tools to recognize and effectively respond to mental health crises.* PESI Publishing.

Bush, K., Kivlahan, D. R., McDonell, M. B., Fihn, S. D., & Bradley, K. A., for the Ambulatory Care Quality Improvement Project (ACQUIP). (1998). The AUDIT alcohol consumption questions (AUDIT-C): An effective brief screening test for problem drinking. *Archives of Internal Medicine, 158*(16), 1789–1795. https://doi.org/10.1001/archinte.158.16.1789.

Center for Substance Abuse Treatment. (2000). Comprehensive case management for substance abuse treatment. *Treatment Improvement Protocol (TIP) Series, 27.* https://store.samhsa.gov/sites/default/files/d7/priv/sma15-4215.pdf.

Center for Substance Abuse Treatment. (2015). Substance abuse treatment and family therapy. *Treatment Improvement Protocol (TIP) Series, 39.* http://lib.adai.washington.edu/clearinghouse/downloads/TIP-39-Substance-Abuse-Treatment-and-Family-Therapy-55.pdf

Confidentiality of Substance Use Disorder Patient Records, 42 C.F.R. § 2.31 (2020).

Confidentiality of Substance Use Disorder Patient Records, 42 C.F.R. § 2.51 (2020).

Danzer, G. S. (2019). *Therapist self-disclosure: An evidence-based guide for practitioners.* Routledge; Taylor & Francis Group.

Frances, A. (2013). *Essentials of psychiatric diagnosis: Responding to the challenges of DSM-5.* The Guilford Press.

Frances, R. J., Miller, S. I., & Mack, A. H. (Eds.). (2005). *Clinical textbook of addictive disorders* (3rd ed.). The Guilford Press.

Friesen, J. G., Wilder, E. J., Bierling, A. M., Koepcke, R., & Poole, M. (2013). *Living from the heart that Jesus gave you.* Shepherd's House, Inc.

Gregorowski, C., Seedat, S., & Jordaan, G. P. (2013). A clinical approach to the assessment and management of co-morbid eating disorders and substance use disorders. *BioMed Central Psychiatry, 13*(1), 1–12.

Grisel, J. (2019). *Never enough: The neuroscience and experience of addiction.* Doubleday.

Hardin, R. (Ed.) (2013). *SMART recovery handbook: Tools and strategies to help you on your recovery journey* (3rd ed.). Alcohol and Drug Abuse Self Help Network, Inc.

Hari, J. (2015). *Chasing the scream: The first and last days of the war on drugs.* Bloomsbury Publishing.

Herron, A. J., & Brennan, T. K. (2015). *The ASAM essentials of addiction medicine* (2nd ed.). Lippincott Williams & Wilkins.

Herron, A. J., & Brennan, T. K. (2020). *The ASAM essentials of addiction medicine* (3rd ed.). Lippincott Williams & Wilkins.

Inaba, D. S., & Cohen, W. E. (2014). *Uppers, downers, all arounders: Physical and mental effects of psychoactive drugs* (8th ed.). CNS Productions, Inc.

Jakubowski, A. & Fox, A. (2020). "Defining low-threshold buprenorphine treatment." *Journal of Addiction Medicine, March/April 2020, 14*(2), 95–98.

Joudrey, P. J., Khan, M. R., Wang, E. A., Scheidell, J. D., Edelman, E. J., McInnes, D. K., & Fox, A. D. (2019). A conceptual model for understanding post-release opioid-related overdose risk. *Addiction Science & Clinical Practice, 14*(1), 1–14. https://doi.org/10.1186/s13722-019-0145-5.

Kavanaugh, P. R., & McLean, K. (2020). Motivations for diverted buprenorphine use in a multisite qualitative study. *Journal of Drug Issues, 50*(4), 550–565. https://doi.org/10.1177/0022042620941796.

Levine, P. A. (2015). *Trauma and memory: Brain and body in a search for the living past: A practical guide for understanding and working with traumatic memory.* North American Books.

Lua, J., Olney, L. & Isles, C. (2019). Cannabis hyperemesis syndrome: Still under recognized after all these years. *Journal of the Royal College of Physicians of Edinburgh, 49*(2), 132–134.

Macy, B. (2018). *Dopesick: Dealers, doctors, and the drug company that addicted America.* Little, Brown and Company.

Manatt. (2020). Policy Brief: "SAMHSA finalizes revisions to substance use disorder confidentiality regulations (Part 2); Defers more sweeping changes until 2021." *Manatt Insights,* July 17, 2020.

Maté, G. (2010). *In the realm of hungry ghosts: Close encounters with addiction.* North Atlantic Books.

McQueen, K., & Murphy-Oikonen, J. (2016). Neonatal abstinence syndrome. *New England Journal of Medicine, 375*(25), 2468–2478.

Mee-Lee, D., Shulman, G. D., Fishman, M. J., Gastfriend, D. R., Miller, M. M., & Provence, S. M. (Eds.). (2013). *The ASAM criteria: Treatment criteria for addictive, substance-related, co-occurring conditions* (3rd ed.). The Change Companies.

Meyers, R. J., Miller, W. R., Hill, D. E., & Tonigan, J. S. (1998). Community reinforcement and family training (CRAFT): Engaging unmotivated drug users in treatment. *Journal of Substance Abuse, 10*(3), 291–308. https://doi.org/10.1016/S0899-3289(99)00003-6.

Morgan, O. J. (2019). *Addiction, attachment, trauma and recovery: The power of connection* (Norton Series on Interpersonal Neurobiology). W. W. Norton & Company.

Pollan, M. (2018). *How to change your mind: What the new science of psychedelics teaches us about consciousness, dying, addiction, depression, and transcendence.* Penguin Books.

Prins, A., Bovin, M. J., Kimerling, R., Kaloupek, D. G., Marx, B. P., Pless Kaiser, A., & Schnurr, P. P. (2015). *The Primary Care PTSD Screen for DSM-5 (PC-PTSD-5).* [Measurement instrument].

Prochaska, J. O. & Velicer, W. F. (1997). The transtheoretical model of behavior change. *American Journal of Health Promotion, 12*(1), 38–48. https://doi.org/10.4278/0890-1171-12.1.38.

Quinn, G. (2010). Institutional denial or minimization: Substance abuse training in social work education. *Substance Abuse, 31*(1), 8–11. https://doi.org/10.1080/08897070903442475.

Quinones, S. (2015). *Dreamland: The true tale of America's opioid epidemic.* Bloomsbury Publishing USA.

Radley, D. C., Baumgartner, J. C., Collins, S. R., Zephyrin, L., & Schneider, E. C. (2021). Achieving racial and ethnic equity in U.S. healthcare: A score of state performance. *The Commonwealth Fund.* https://www.commonwealthfund.org/publications/scorecard/2021/nov/achieving-racial-ethnic-equity-us-health-care-state-performance.

Russell, M. (1994). New assessment tools for risk drinking during pregnancy: T-ACE, TWEAK, and others. *Alcohol Health and Research World, 18*(1), 55–61.

Sadock, B. J., Sadock, V. A., & Ruiz, P. (2015). *Kaplan & Sadock's synopsis of psychiatry: Behavioral sciences/clinical psychiatry* (11th ed.). Wolters Kluwer.

Seitz, S. & Waterman, C. (2020, February 27). Privacy in data sharing [Paper presentation]. *National Association for State Health Policy by Center of Excellence for Protected Health Information,* Atlanta, GA, United States.

Sharp, C. W., Beauvais, F., & Spence, R. T. (Eds.). (1992). National Institute on Drug Abuse, Research Monograph Series 129: Inhalant abuse: A volatile research agenda. *Department of Health and Human Services.*

Skinner, H. A. (1982). *The Drug Abuse Screening Test. Addictive Behaviors, 7*(4), 363–371. https://doi.org/10.1016/0306-4603(82)90005-3.

Sokol, R. J., Martier, S. S., & Ager, J. W. (1989). The T-ACE questions: Practical prenatal detection of risk-drinking. *American Journal of Obstetrics and Gynecology, 160*(4), 863–870. https://doi.org/10.1016/0002-9378(89)90302-5.

Substance Abuse and Mental Health Services Administration. (2012). Substance abuse treatment: Group therapy inservice training (Based on treatment improvement protocol TIP series, 41). *U.S. Department of Health and Human Services*. http://integratedrecovery.org/wp-content/uploads/2019/12/TIP41-SAT.Group_.Therapy .Inservice.Training.pdf.

Substance Abuse and Mental Health Services Administration. (2017). Guidelines for successful transition of people with mental or substance use disorders from jail or prison: Implementation guide. *U.S. Department of Health and Human Services*. https://store.samhsa.gov/sites/default/files/d7/priv/sma16-4998.pdf.

Substance Abuse and Mental Health Services Administration. (2020). Substance use disorder treatment for people with co-occurring disorders. *Treatment Improvement Protocol (TIP) Series, 42*. https://store.samhsa .gov/sites/default/files/SAMHSA_Digital_Download/PEP20-02-01-004_Final_508.pdf.

Substance Abuse and Mental Health Services Administration. (2020, January 14). 2018 national survey on drug use and health: Lesbian, gay, & bisexual (LGB) adults. *U.S. Department of Health and Human Services*. https://www.samhsa.gov/data/report/2018-nsduh-lesbian-gay-bisexual-lgb-adults.

Sullivan, J. T., Sykora, K., Schneiderman, J., Naranjo, C. A., & Sellers, E. M. (1989). Assessment of alcohol withdrawal: The revised clinical institute withdrawal assessment for alcohol scale (CIWA-Ar). *British Journal of Addiction, 84*(11), 1353–1357. https://doi.org/10.1111/j.1360-0443.1989.tb00737.x.

Szalavitz, M. (2021). *Undoing drugs: The untold story of harm reduction and the future of addiction*. Hachette Books.

Trivdei, M. H., Walker, R., Ling, W., dela Cruz, A., Sharma, G., Carmody, T., Ghitza, U. E., Wahle, A., Kim, M., Shores-Wilson, K., Sparenborg, S., Coffin, P., Schmitz, J., Wiest, K., Bart, G., Sonne, S. C., Wakhlu, S., Rush, A. J., Nunes, E. V., & Shoptaw, S. (2021). Bupropion and naltrexone in methamphetamine disorder. *The New England Journal of Medicine, 384*(2), 140–153. https://doi.org/10.1056/NEJMoa2020214.

van der Kolk, B. A. (2014). *The body keeps the score: Brain, mind, and body in the healing of trauma*. Penguin Books.

W., B. (2018). *Twelve secular steps: An addiction recovery guide*. Beowulf Press, LLC.

Wesson, D. R., & Ling, W. (2003). The clinical opiate withdrawal scale (COWS). *Journal of Psychoactive Drugs, 35*(2), 253–259.

West, R. (2012). *Theory of addiction*. Wiley, John & Sons, Inc.

Westhoff, B. (2019). *Fentanyl, Inc.: How rogue chemists are creating the deadliest wave of the opioid epidemic*. Atlantic Monthly Press.

White, W. L. (2014). *Slaying the dragon: The history of addiction treatment and recovery in America* (2nd ed.). Chestnut Health Services.

White, W. L. (2017). *Recovery rising: A retrospective of addiction treatment and recovery advocacy*. Rita Chaney.

Wilkey, C., Lundgren, L., & Amodeo, M. (2013). Addiction training in social work schools: A nationwide analysis. *Journal of Social Work Practice in the Addictions, 13*(2), 192–210. https://doi.org/10.1080/1533256X .2013.785872.

Winstock, A., Mitchenson, L., Ramsey, J., Davies, S., Puchnarewicz, M., & Marsden, J. (2011). Mephedrone: Use, subjective effects and health risks. *Addiction, 106*(11), 1991–1996. https://doi.org/10.1111/j.1360 -0443.2011.03502.x.

Wright, F. D., Beck, A. T., Newman, C. F. & Liese, B. S. (1993). Cognitive therapy of substance abuse: Theoretical rationale. *Behavioral Treatments for Drug Abuse and Dependence, 137,* 123–146.

Yalom, I. D. (1995). *The theory and practice of group psychotherapy* (4th ed.). Basic Books.

Made in the USA
Las Vegas, NV
23 November 2024

12515059R00195